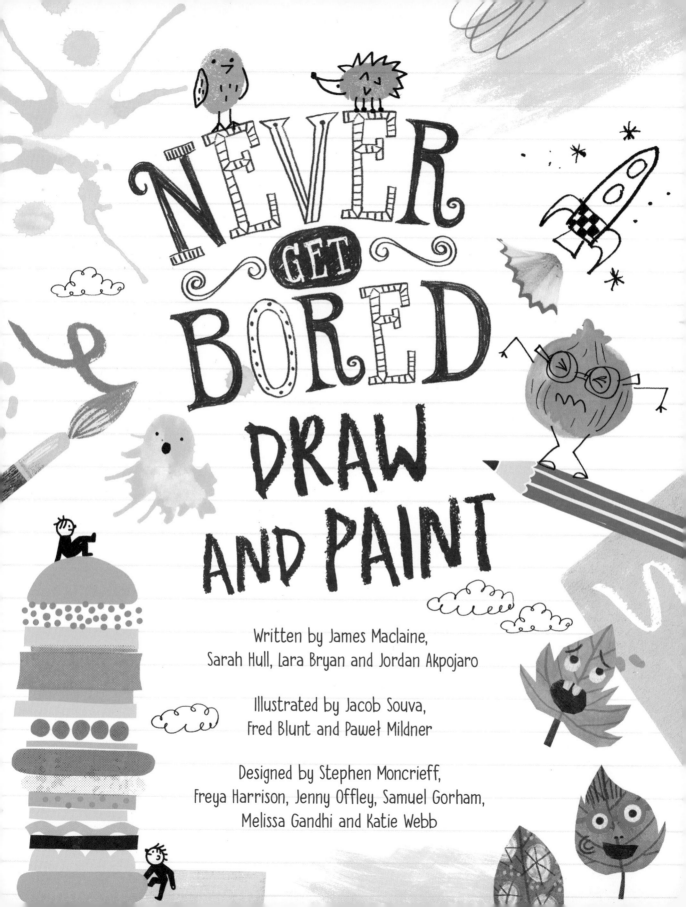

NEVER GET BORED

DRAW AND PAINT

Written by James Maclaine,
Sarah Hull, Lara Bryan and Jordan Akpojaro

Illustrated by Jacob Souva,
Fred Blunt and Paweł Mildner

Designed by Stephen Moncrieff,
Freya Harrison, Jenny Offley, Samuel Gorham,
Melissa Gandhi and Katie Webb

FEELING BORED?

Then, find your drawing and painting things, and give these boredom-busting techniques a try...

1 Doodle big birds on lots of pieces of paper.

Arrange them together to make a flock.

2 Squash a painting.

Drip a few drops of runny paints in the middle of a piece of paper.

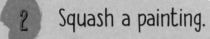

Fold the paper in half and press down on it with your fingertips. Then reveal what's inside...

Use a pen to turn your painting into a butterfly or a monster – or something else.

3 Imagine strange combinations of things and make pictures of them.

for example...

a pink shark in a teacup

How absurd!

sandwiches for shoes

4 Paint rectangles in a row, then turn them into skyscrapers.

Wait for the paint to dry before you draw windows on top.

5 Paint with two paints at once.

Dip one side of your paintbrush in one paint and the other side in another.

Then, paint flower shapes.

And that was only to get you started!

You'll discover lots more ideas throughout this book.

Just flip through the book's pages, open it at random, or browse the contents on pages 4–5.

There are some puzzles inside, too. You'll find the solutions to them on pages 94–95.

INSTEAD OF GETTING BORED...

Discover lots of printing techniques on pages 24-25, 70-71 and 88-89.

You'll find drawing games to play on pages 16-17, 32-33, 72 and 77.

Take inspiration from famous artists — see pages 6, 15, 34-35, 56 and 82-83.

TAKE A LINE FOR A WALK

Draw a continuous line over a piece of paper to make lots of pictures and patterns. Keep your pen or pencil on the paper at all times and use these ideas to inspire you.

You could cut out shapes and stick them on your paper to draw over too.

Draw the parts of a face...

...buildings and all their windows...

...a fluttering butterfly...

LINE ARTIST

Swiss artist Paul Klee (1879–1940) often painted and drew continuous lines in his pictures.

The only mistake you can make when drawing like this is to lift your pen off the paper.

...a spotted dalmatian...

He described drawing as...

An active line on a walk, moving freely, without a goal. A walk for a walk's sake.

...and a crescent moon next to some stars.

6

DOODLE NEVER-ENDING TRIANGLES

It's surprisingly easy to draw a mind-boggling pattern of triangles. Just follow the steps on this page.

1 Place a piece of white paper over this picture of a six-sided shape called a hexagon. The paper needs to be thin enough for you to see the hexagon through it. Draw over all the thick blue lines.

This hexagon is made up of six triangles.

The arrows on this picture show you which direction to draw your patterns in.

2 Start your pattern in triangle 1. Draw a smaller triangle inside it like this, line by line.

Draw in a clockwise direction.

3 Keep drawing smaller and smaller triangles in the same way, in a clockwise spiral...

...until there's no space left.

4 Now draw another spiral of triangles within triangles, in triangle 2. Draw the lines in the opposite direction.

The finished pattern should look like this...

5 Repeat this technique in triangles 3, 4, 5, then 6. Change the direction of the spiral each time.

Together, the alternating spirals of triangles create a 3D illusion.

DRAW PENGUINS

Follow the tips and ideas on these pages to draw lots of penguin pictures. You'll need some black, yellow, orange and pink colored pencils or felt-tip pens.

Draw each penguin in stages...

1

Draw an egg shape first...

2

...then a smaller egg shape inside and a head...

3

...two wings and two feet...

4

...and an eye and a beak.

Then, fill it in.

You could vary your drawings to show several different types of penguins...

GENTOO

Fill in a Gentoo penguin's beak and feet with orange.

Add some yellow details around its face.

EMPEROR

For an Emperor penguin, start with an egg shape that's tall and big.

CHICKS

Draw lots of little lines to show baby penguins' fluffy feathers.

Draw two parts for an open beak.

ANTARCTIC ART

You could make a scene for your penguin pictures like the one on these pages. Cut out a shape from white paper for an iceberg and wide strips from different shades of blue paper for the sea and sky. Arrange them on a large piece of paper before you glue them down.

8

DRAW SWIMMING PENGUINS, TOO...

1 first draw an egg shape, tilted on its side.

2 Then, add these shapes...

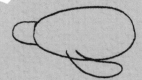

3 ...and a beak, eye, tail and feet.

CHINSTRAP

A chinstrap penguin has a thin black line under its face. Its feet are pink.

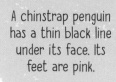

MACARONI

Draw yellow spiky lines to add a macaroni penguin's crest.

ADÉLIE

Leave a small white ring around an Adélie penguin's eye.

Try drawing penguins at different angles when they're diving into the sea.

Use a white colored pencil to draw small circles for bubbles.

Copy these fish so your penguins have something to catch.

9

BLOW SPLATS OF PAINT

Mix paint with water to make a runny mixture. Then, use a paper straw to blow it into big splats. Turn the splats into strange creatures by adding details in pen.

 1

First drip some of the mixture from the end of a paintbrush onto a piece of paper.

2

Next, blow through a straw, so that the paint spreads out into a splat.

Move the straw to blow the paint in different directions.

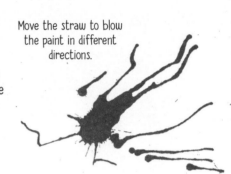

You could use mixtures made from different colored paints to fill your paper with splats. When the paint is dry, draw on each splat to bring it to life...

A bird?

A wobbly flamingo?

A friendly scorpion?

A flying, crested lizard?

A hairy, tap dancing jellyfish?

DESIGN A FIREWORKS DISPLAY

Draw exploding fireworks with wax crayons, then cover the whole piece of paper with water-based paint. The wax and paint don't mix, so the firework pictures gleam and sparkle.

Different types of fireworks are named after plants, animals and things in the night sky that they look like.

PALM

Draw about twelve lines bursting from the same point.

PEONY

Doodle lots of little spots to make a big, round flower shape.

WILLOW

Add small star shapes at the bottom of curved, drooping lines.

CHRYSANTHEMUM

Draw lots of short, straight lines in rings.

You could use two colors alternately for the rings.

FISH

This type of firework gets its name from the way the squiggles "swim" away from the middle.

COMET

Start by drawing a star, then add a shower of dots.

Use black or dark blue paint for the sky. Mix it with some water to make a thin, runny mixture.

BAMBOO BANGERS

The first fireworks were invented in China over a thousand years ago. They were made by packing gunpowder into hollow bamboo stalks.

You could add a skyline of buildings at the bottom with a black pen.

11

FIND INSPIRATION

Sometimes everyone needs a little help getting started with a new painting or drawing. This guide will help you come up with ideas for your pictures.

STEP 1 - FREE YOUR MIND

It's hard to think about art when your head is full of distracting thoughts. So clear your mind to make room for arty ideas...

Sit still and relax.

Close your eyes.

Breathe in slowly through your nose and out through your mouth.

Do any ideas pop into your head?

STEP 2 - LOOK, LOOK, LOOK

There's inspiration all around you. You just need to find it.

STEP 3
GO FOR A WALK

A change of scene could inspire you. You might spot something to draw in the distance, or something small close at hand.

Look up at the clouds. Try doodling their shapes.

If somebody's nearby, you could try doing a portrait.

Zzzzzzzz

Trees on the horizon

You could take photos of things you want to draw for when you get back home.

A snail on the move

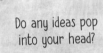

STEP 4 - COPY

Look through books or magazines to find pictures you like. Then, try to copy them.

STEP 5 EXPERIMENT

Experimenting with different ways of making pictures can help you generate ideas.

Close your eyes and draw a squiggle...

...then, open your eyes and turn it into a picture.

You could draw or paint on old newspaper or wrapping paper instead of blank paper.

You can use a chunk of a beet as a smudgy purple pen.

NEWS!

STEP 6 - EMBRACE ACCIDENTS

If you make mistakes, try adapting your pictures to them. Sometimes artists make their most brilliant pictures this way.

French writer and artist Victor Hugo's imaginative drawings often began as blots of ink or smudges.

STEP 7 LISTEN TO MUSIC

Try listening to different types of music and painting at the same time.

Does the music inspire you to use bright or dark colors?

STEP 8 - GET IT DOWN ON PAPER

Sketch or note down any ideas you have quickly, before you forget them.

TESSELLATE

Patterns made up of repeating shapes, without any gaps between them, are known as TESSELLATIONS. The shapes on these pages will help you to draw your own tessellating patterns.

DIAMOND

If you copy the diamond shape below, you can use it to make a pattern of cubes that looks three-dimensional, or 3D.

1 Put a piece of tracing paper or baking parchment over this shape. Use a pencil to draw over the thick black lines.

2 Turn over the paper or parchment and put it on top of a piece of thick paper. Draw over the lines, pressing hard.

3 The pencil lines should now show on the thick paper. Cut out the diamond shape.

4 Put the shape on the paper you want to add patterns to. Then, draw around it.

5 Rotate the shape 90° and line it up with the lower-left side of the diamond you drew in step 4. Draw around it.

6 Turn the shape again so that it fits between the two diamonds. Draw around it to complete a cube.

7 Continue moving and rotating the shape to add rows and rows of cubes, next to each other.

Fill in the cubes with three different shades of blue to make them look more 3D, like this...

By doodling windows and doors you could turn them into houses.

Now, use the same technique to copy and cut out the
turtle and seal shapes below to make even more patterns.

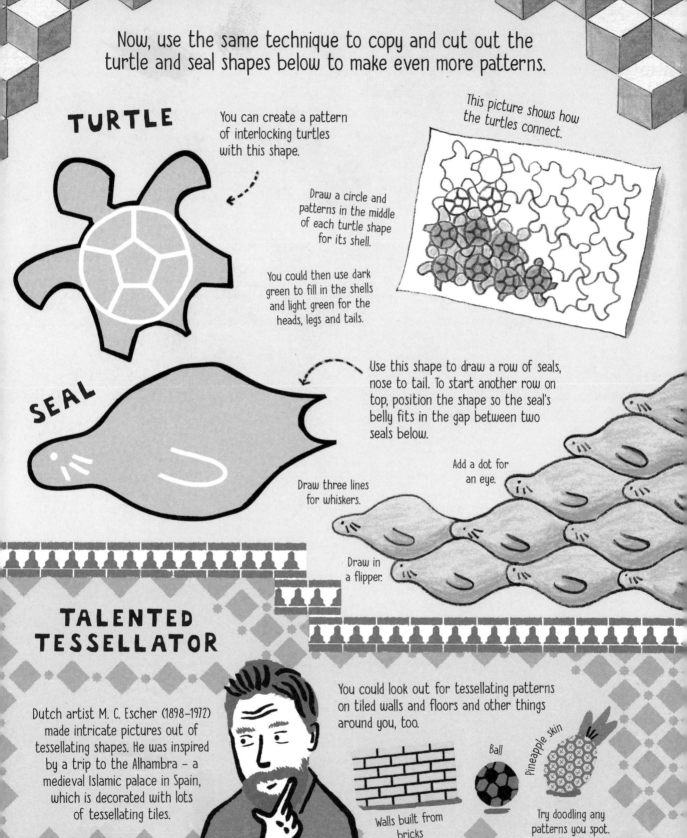

TURTLE

You can create a pattern
of interlocking turtles
with this shape.

This picture shows how
the turtles connect.

Draw a circle and
patterns in the middle
of each turtle shape
for its shell.

You could then use dark
green to fill in the shells
and light green for the
heads, legs and tails.

SEAL

Use this shape to draw a row of seals,
nose to tail. To start another row on
top, position the shape so the seal's
belly fits in the gap between two
seals below.

Draw three lines
for whiskers.

Add a dot for
an eye.

Draw in
a flipper.

TALENTED
TESSELLATOR

Dutch artist M. C. Escher (1898–1972)
made intricate pictures out of
tessellating shapes. He was inspired
by a trip to the Alhambra – a
medieval Islamic palace in Spain,
which is decorated with lots
of tessellating tiles.

You could look out for tessellating patterns
on tiled walls and floors and other things
around you, too.

Ball

Pineapple skin

Walls built from
bricks

Try doodling any
patterns you spot.

15

DRAW EXTRAORDINARY OUTFITS

Put together surprising combinations of clothes by
playing this drawing game with two or more friends.
You each need a pen and a piece of paper.

1 Draw a head at the top of your paper.

You could add a hat or hair accessories, makeup or glasses, earrings or a necklace.

Fold down the paper leaving the bottom of the neck just visible. Then, trade pieces of paper.

2 Next, draw a body in a fancy jacket or top. Stop just above the legs.

Fold the paper again, so only the bottom of the body is visible. Then, pass it on.

3 Add pants, shorts or a skirt on a pair of legs. Stop at the ankles.

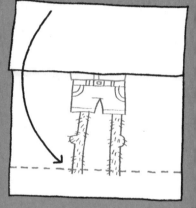

Fold the paper, leaving just the bottom of the ankles showing. Then, trade papers again.

OLD FASHIONS

Read about some curious trends from history. Maybe they could inspire your drawings when you're playing the game above?

Extravagant wigs became hugely popular in France in the 17th and 18th centuries.

In Venice, around 500 years ago, people wore super-high shoes called "chopines," to keep their clothes from trailing in dirt.

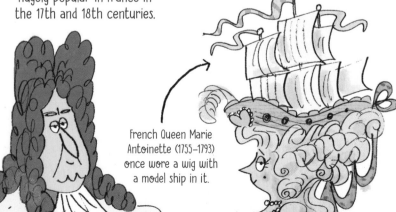

French Queen Marie Antoinette (1755–1793) once wore a wig with a model ship in it.

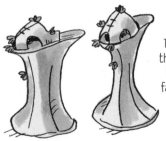

The higher the chopine, the more fashionable!

4 Finish off the drawing with some footwear.

How about some silky slippers? Or, maybe, socks and sandals?

Fold the paper again to hide your drawing, then pass it on.

5 Everyone unfolds the paper at once to reveal the outfits.

Such style!

Your coat is goooorgeous!

I LOVE your shoes.

Wealthy women in ancient Egypt wore cones of perfumed wax or fat on their heads as a sort of deodorant.

Droopy sleeves were in fashion across western Europe around 900 years ago.

Shoulder pads were fashionable in the 16th century.

English King Henry VIII (1491–1547) also wore padding on his arms and legs to make himself look bigger and more impressive.

MIX YOUR OWN PAINTS

Here are several different "recipes" for making your own paints.
They use vegetable scraps and things you might find in the kitchen.
Be careful – these paints could stain your clothes or work surfaces.

Curry yellow

Put two heaped teaspoons of turmeric or curry powder in a mug.

Half fill the mug with warm water and mix well.

Beet pink

Drain the juice from a package of cooked beets or a jar of pickled beets.

Coffee brown

Mix three heaped teaspoons of instant coffee with some hot water in a mug.

Spinach green

A handful of spinach leaves

To make the four paints on the right, follow the same two steps below with each ingredient.

1. Put the skins or leaves in a pan with some water. Heat the pan until the water boils, then let it simmer for 15 minutes.

Onion orange

Skins of three brown onions

2. Leave the mixture to cool, then strain the liquid through a sieve into a bowl or jar.

Paint

Cabbage blue

Use the outer leaves of a red cabbage, roughly chopped.

Heat red cabbage leaves in the pan for only 5–10 minutes to make blue paint.

Cabbage purple

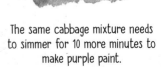

The same cabbage mixture needs to simmer for 10 more minutes to make purple paint.

18

If you're not going to use the paints right away, you can store them in sealed jars for a week or so.

Maybe you could paint a gang of vegetable monsters with your paints?

Paint these different shapes and wait for them to dry. Then add faces and other details with a black pen.

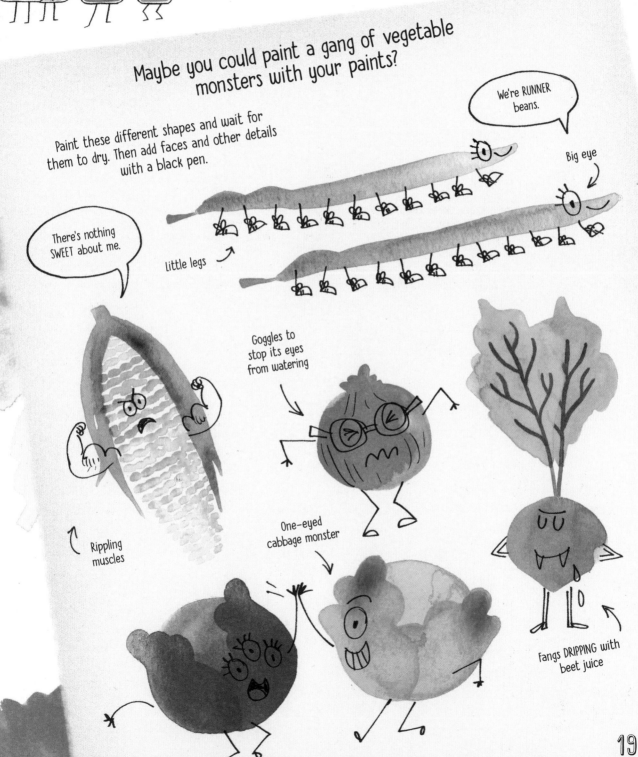

We're RUNNER beans.

Big eye

There's nothing SWEET about me.

Little legs

Goggles to stop its eyes from watering

One-eyed cabbage monster

Rippling muscles

Fangs DRIPPING with beet juice

DOODLE ON MAGAZINES

You could use a black felt-tip marker to transform pictures in an old magazine. leaf through the pages and let your imagination run wild.

Scribble shapes and patterns over a front cover.

Insert unexpected details in a travel photo.

pets

MONTHLY

10 Training tips for beginners

FIND YOURSELF

AND SO MUCH MORE...

STYLE **VIEW**

MOODY STREETWEAR

HOW TO TAKE FASHION *SERIOUSLY*

EXCLUSIVE REVIEW
WHO WON SHOE DESIGNER OF THE YEAR?

Give someone a historic makeover.

SOUND OF THE SUMMER
THE HOTTEST TRACKS

Add some friendly monsters to a furniture advertisement.

-50%

SPRING Furniture **SALE**

DRAW JAW-DROPPING PORTRAITS

With some folded pieces of paper and pens, you can draw pictures that reveal surprises when you open them up.

You need to fold and unfold each piece of paper before *and* as you draw.

1 First, fold the paper in half, from the top narrow edge to the bottom.

2 Fold in half again.

3 Then, open up the paper...

4 ...and fold it together, like this, so the middle two sections are hidden.

5 Draw a face in the top and bottom sections, across the fold.

6 Open up the paper. Now, draw the "hidden" part of your picture in the middle.

You could draw a picture based on the one above – or the others on the right.

GREEDY MONSTER

MOUTHFUL OF BIRDS

FIREBREATHING MOUSE

EQUIP YOUR STUDIO

You can turn anywhere into an artist's studio by making these items of equipment. They're easy to make, re-using things that you might otherwise throw away.

FOLD-UP EASEL

This stand supports the pictures you're painting. It folds away when you're not using it.

YOU'LL NEED...

- three large pieces of thick cardboard
- masking tape
- two long pieces of string
- two large paper clips
- thick paper
- glue
- clear tape

1 Cut out two large rectangles of cardboard, the same size as each other.

They need to be wider and taller than the pictures you're planning to make.

2 Place the large rectangles end to end, then join them together with thick strips of masking tape.

The strips should go this way... ----> ...and this way.

3 Turn over both rectangles, to tape them on the other side too.

4 Now fold the rectangles together. They should line up neatly. If the sides overlap, trim them with scissors.

5 Push a pencil through both rectangles to make holes in the bottom corners.

6 Thread one of the pieces of string through the holes on the left-hand side. Tie a big knot at one end.

7 Tie a big knot at the other end too, so the string is tight when you open and stand up the easel, like this. Repeat steps 6 and 7 with the second piece of string on the other side.

The knot needs to be bigger than the hole.

8 Cut a strip of thick paper and glue it over the masking tape at the top of your easel.

The paper clips need to be this way around, so you can use them to hold paper you draw or paint on.

9 Open up the paper clips a little. Thread a piece of clear tape inside each one to stick them to the strip you added in step 8.

10 Cut out a rectangle from the third piece of cardboard, to slot inside the base of your easel. This keeps it sturdy.

The rectangle needs to be longer than the width of your easel and as wide as the gap between the front and back.

HOW TO FOLD AWAY

Close your easel, storing the base rectangle, tucked inside it. You can tie a bow with each piece of string to keep it shut.

PAINT PALETTE

Some artists put the paints they're using on a thin board, called a palette. To make your own, you'll need a large piece of cardboard and at least six bottle caps.

1 Draw a shape on the cardboard that looks like this. Then cut it out.

2 Use glue to stick the bottle caps on top, open side up. When the glue is dry, you can fill each cap with a small squirt of liquid paint.

It needs to be about the same size as a dinner plate.

Hold your palette with the hand you're not using to paint. You could push a pen through the cardboard, then cut out a hole for your thumb to grip.

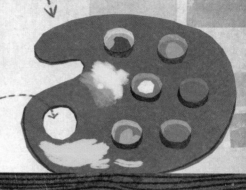

WATER JARS

Save old jars then fill them with water for cleaning your brushes.

leave your brushes somewhere to dry after you've cleaned them.

Brush water

CONTAINERS AND HOLDERS

Join together old cardboard tubes by wrapping tape around them, to make containers for your pencils.

Old cans and plant pots are good places to keep your tools too.

Make holes in the lid of a shoebox with the pointed end of a pencil.

PAINT TRAY

You could also turn an old egg carton into a tray for liquid paints.

Then, push in pens, pencils, crayons or brushes to make holes wide enough for each one.

You could decorate the pots with paints.

PRINT WITH YOUR FINGERS

If you can find an old sponge and some paint, you can make fun pictures just with your fingers and hands.

First...

Cut the sponge into pieces for different colors. Then, brush thin layers of paint onto the sponge pieces. Press your fingers on them before you make prints on paper.

Clean your fingers on a paper towel when you want to use a different color.

You can use different parts of your fingers to make different-sized prints.

Thumb

Index finger

Finger tip

Side of finger

After the paint has dried, draw details with a pen to turn each print into a bird, a leaf, or anything else you like.

Flyaway balloons

You can use fingerprints to make balloons. When the paint is dry, add some strings and someone clinging on.

Spiny hedgehogs

Draw zigzags or little lines for spines.

Leafy tree

Use a brown felt-tip pen to draw a tree trunk and branches. Add a big circle with a green pen on top, then fill it with leaves.

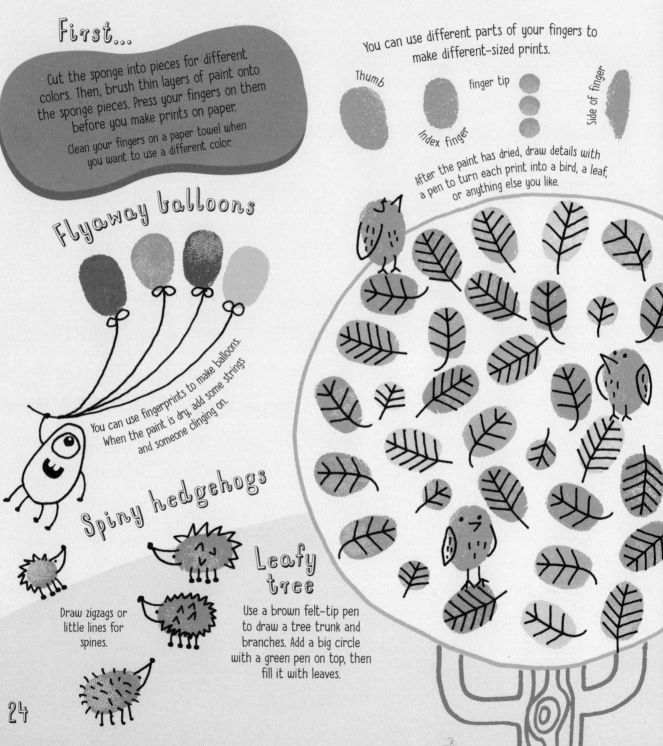

24

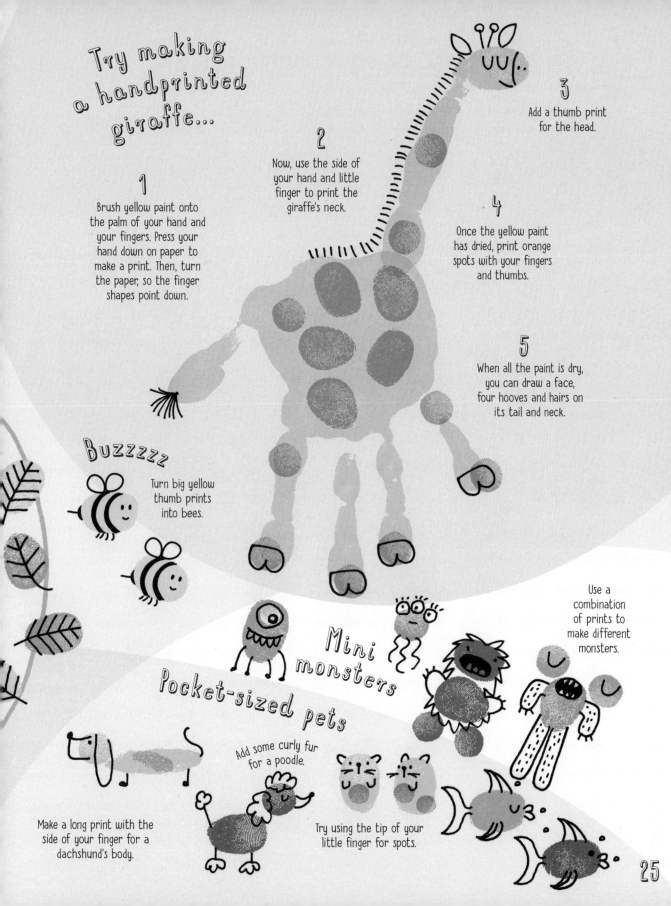

Try making a handprinted giraffe...

1

Brush yellow paint onto the palm of your hand and your fingers. Press your hand down on paper to make a print. Then, turn the paper, so the finger shapes point down.

2

Now, use the side of your hand and little finger to print the giraffe's neck.

3

Add a thumb print for the head.

4

Once the yellow paint has dried, print orange spots with your fingers and thumbs.

5

When all the paint is dry, you can draw a face, four hooves and hairs on its tail and neck.

Buzzzzz

Turn big yellow thumb prints into bees.

Mini monsters

Use a combination of prints to make different monsters.

Pocket-sized pets

Make a long print with the side of your finger for a dachshund's body.

Add some curly fur for a poodle.

Try using the tip of your little finger for spots.

DRAW WILD ANIMALS

Follow all the steps to draw these animals. Then use felt-tip pens or colored pencils to fill them in.

SLOTH

1 Draw two egg shapes like this.

2 Add an arm and a leg...

3 ...and a branch.

4 Draw another egg shape, two eye patches...

...and some claws.

Did you know that sloths are slow climbers, but they can swim fast?

5 Add eyes, a nose and a mouth...

...and dashes for fur.

LLAMA

Draw steps 1 to 3 in pencil, and step 4 in pen.

1 Draw this shape for a body.

2 Add a head...

...a neck...

3 ...two ears...

...a tail...

...and four legs.

Llamas spit when they're angry or scared.

4 Draw over all the pencil lines with a pen, EXCEPT for the parts below the neck...

...and above the legs.

When the ink is dry, erase the pencil lines. Then, add a face and dashes for fur.

FLAMINGO

1 Draw a leaf shape like this.

2 Draw a curved line, shaped like a "Z."

3 Continue this line to make its head and neck.

Draw a wiggly line for a wing.

4 Add a beak...

...and lines for legs.

5 Give it an eye.

Flamingos stand on one leg, so they can keep their other leg close to their body. This keeps it warm.

Draw these shapes for feet.

ORCA

1 Draw a big leaf shape.

2 Add a fin...

...an eye...

...another fin...

...and a tail.

3 Draw these different shapes around the eye...

...and along its belly.

4 Fill in the rest of your picture with a black pen.

Orcas are also known as killer whales because they hunt sea lions – and other whales.

27

MAKE A MAP

Can you create a map of an imaginary world? First make a large piece of paper look like an old material called parchment (see right), then illustrate it with some of the ideas on these pages...

FROM PAPER TO "PARCHMENT"

1 Stir a cup of warm water with a teabag or some instant coffee.

2 Then, use a paintbrush to paint the liquid over a piece of paper. Wait for it to dry.

3 To make the paper look old, wad it up, then open it out again. You could tear the edges a little, too.

Draw lines in green for the edges of different islands.

Giant's City

Add tall buildings, houses or a castle, where people or monsters live.

Write on fantastical place names.

Salt Tears Sea

Craggy Cascade

Maybe you could draw a hot-air balloon?

Doodle sand dunes for a blistering desert.

Add icy mountains...

You could make up a story set in this fantasy world. Write it down on another piece of paper.

Skytop Range

...or an erupting volcano.

Mountain of Fire

NOW ADD A BIKE

Maybe you could invent a bike to go on a journey around your map? Follow these steps, then customize it with features of your choice.

1 Draw two parallel lines, with a handlebar and seat at the top.

2 Add two lines to create a triangle shape between them.

3 Draw two lines to make a smaller triangle at the back.

4 Draw two circles for wheels, then add lines for spokes.

5 For the chain, draw a circle like this. Add black lines to connect it to the middle of the back wheel.

6 Complete your invention with some of these ideas, or invent your own...

Propeller   Wings   Robot arms   Sail

DRAW SKULLS AND SKELETONS

Follow the steps on this page to doodle different types of skulls and skeletons with a black pen.

Doodles don't need to look too neat. They have more character if they look a little scribbled.

SKULL

To draw a skull, start with this shape first.

Doodle some eyes and a nose.

Add vertical lines for its mouth.

Draw a small rectangle underneath.

TYRANNOSAURUS REX

Copy the two big shapes for this dinosaur skull.

Draw holes for an eye and a nose, then fill them in.

Add two rows of zigzags for teeth.

Doodle narrow ovals for neck bones.

You could copy these skulls as well. Then, color them in.

FISH

Draw a triangle for its skull...

Draw overlapping curved lines for its spine.

...and a circle inside it. Then, shade around it.

Add ribs...

...and a fan shape for its tail.

X-RAY YOUR HAND

You can't SEE the bones inside your body without the help of an X-ray machine. But you could DRAW a picture to reveal the bones in your right hand.

Use black paper and a white colored pencil or chalk to make your picture look like an X-ray.

1
Place your right hand on the paper and draw around it.

2
Copy the outlines of all the bone shapes inside this hand picture onto yours. There are 27 bones in total.

3
Fill in all the bone shapes. Press your colored pencil or chalk firmly.

4
Then, shade the rest of your hand shape LIGHTLY, around the bones.

If you don't have any black paper...

You could shade over a piece of paper with an ordinary pencil. Then, place your right hand on top and rub a small eraser around it to remove some of the pencil markings. Use the eraser to show the bone shapes too.

The eraser at the end of some types of pencils works well.

Handy X-rays

The first ever X-ray photograph was taken by a German scientist named Wilhelm Röntgen in 1895. It showed his wife's hand.

31

PLAY DRAWING GAMES

You can draw AND play at the same time with these games for one or more players.

AGAINST THE CLOCK

Challenge a friend to a drawing race. You'll each need a pen and a piece of paper.

1 Set a timer for one minute or ask someone else to watch the clock for you.

2 The idea is for both players to try to draw as many individual stick figures as they can in the time.

Each stick figure needs a circle for a head, two dots for eyes, a line for a body, two arms and two legs.

The stick figures can't hold hands, overlap or touch.

At the end, count how many figures are on each piece of paper. Whoever drew the most is the winner.

ANYONE'S GUESS

This game is for three or more players.

1 First, tear a piece of paper into 20 or so little strips. Write the name of an OBJECT, ANIMAL or PERSON on each strip.

Max's Dad

fork

poodle

Baseball cap

LADYBUG

2 Then, fold the strips in half and put them inside a hat or a bowl.

3 One player picks out a strip and draws a picture, so the other players can guess the word.

 LADYBUG

A ball?

A pizza?

Is it a ladybug?

YES!

The person drawing isn't allowed to say ANYTHING until someone guesses correctly.

4 Whoever guesses the word keeps the strip and draws the next picture. If no one gets it right, the person drawing discards the strip and picks another to draw.

5 Keep playing until there are no names left to draw and guess. The winner is the player with the MOST STRIPS.

SCRIBBLE SEARCH

You can play this game on your own, or with friends.

Draw lots and lots of squiggles and swirling lines on a piece of paper in pencil or pencil crayon.

Then look carefully at the tangled lines you drew. Can you find any shapes or pictures unexpectedly hidden in them?

If you're playing in a group, ask the players to draw their squiggles first, then trade pieces of paper to make pictures.

Use a black pen to draw over anything you spot.

You could add extra details too.

ROLL FUNNY FACES

This is a one-player game, but you'll need a dice as well as a pen and some paper.

Start by drawing a large egg shape for a head...

...then roll the dice four times to continue your picture, copying the examples below.

The number you roll each time decides what you'll copy:

1ST ROLL OF THE DICE

2ND ROLL

3RD ROLL

4TH ROLL

There are **1,296 DIFFERENT FACES** that you can draw playing this game.

TRAIN TO BE A RENAISSANCE ARTIST

The Renaissance was a time in history – about 700 to 400 years ago – when artists in Italy and other parts of Europe had many new ideas and created amazing works of art. Try your hand at these challenges to see if you have what it takes. All you need is a pencil and some paper.

During the Renaissance, if you wanted to become an artist, you had to start as an apprentice in the studio of a great artist. There was lots to learn...

1 MIXING PAINTS

There were no ready-made paints to buy, so apprentices had to learn how to make them using different ingredients...

Orpiment Verdigris Cinnabar Charcoal

Ocher Smalt Lead

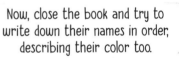

Can you memorize these seven ingredients in 30 seconds?

Now, close the book and try to write down their names in order, describing their color too.

2 COPYCAT

Apprentices learned to draw and paint by copying statues and drawings, or even by drawing each other.

How keen is your eye for detail? Look at these pictures closely. Which apprentice has copied the pose best?

You could also copy the man and bird onto a piece of paper yourself.

A   B   C

3 PRACTICE MAKES PERFECT

Renaissance artists strove for perfection and loved to show off their skills.

It's very difficult to draw a perfect circle, but one Italian artist, Giotto (1267–1337), was incredibly good at it. He impressed the head of the Catholic Church, Pope Boniface VIII, so much, that Boniface asked him to paint many important pictures.

Can you draw a perfectly round circle?

You're not allowed to draw around anything or use a compass.

Draw circles again and again, then compare the results.

4 TRICK THE EYE

Some Renaissance artists painted insects that looked so lifelike viewers thought they were real.

There's a fly on your painting...

Actually, it's a painted trick known as TROMPE L'OEIL – that's French for "tricking the eye."

Try to draw a fly that looks so realistic it fools your friends.

Make sure your fly is life-size, like this one.

Adding a shadow will make your fly look MORE lifelike.

5 LASTLY, SIGN YOUR WORK

If you're going to become a great artist, you'll need to sign your works.

So, use these Renaissance artists' signatures as inspiration to help you invent your own.

You could write your name in full, in capital letters, like Italian artist Lavinia Fontana (1552–1614)...

LAVINIA FONTANA

...or create a stylish design from your initials, like German artist Albrecht Dürer (1471–1528). This is called a monogram.

Artists started to sign their work for the first time during the Renaissance.

DRAW OPTICAL ILLUSIONS

Follow the steps on these pages to draw pictures
that play tricks on your eyes.

POP OUT

Try this technique to create an illusion of a hovering sphere.

1

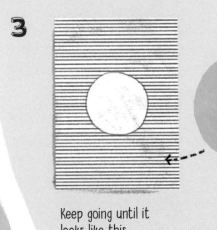

Put a cup upside down in the
middle of a piece of paper.
Draw around it in pencil.

2

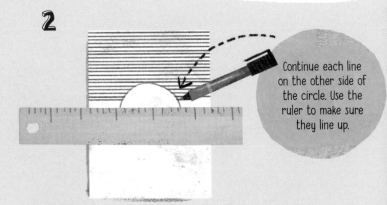

Continue each line
on the other side of
the circle. Use the
ruler to make sure
they line up.

With a ruler, use a red and blue pen alternately to draw
horizontal lines across the paper. Leave small gaps between
the lines. Don't draw inside the circle.

3

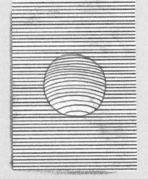

The more lines
you draw, the
better the
illusion looks.

Keep going until it
looks like this.

4

Now look at
your picture.
The circle
should look 3D.

Next draw red or blue
curved lines to connect
the lines on either side
of the circle.

You could draw
around other
objects in step 1,
to make different
hovering shapes.

Turn to page 1 to find out how to draw a 3D pattern of triangles.

3D HOLE

Make a hole appear in a piece of paper by drawing a square and some lines. You could use a ruler to help you draw and measure the lines, but they don't have to be too neat.

1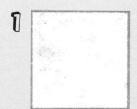

Use a pencil to draw a square in the MIDDLE of the paper. Each side should be about 9cm (3.5in) long.

2

Draw a diagonal line from the bottom corner to the top.

3

Draw a line about 1cm (0.5in) above the bottom edge, from the right to the diagonal line.

4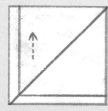

Continue the line up to the top, about 1cm (0.5in) from the left edge.

5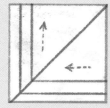

Repeat steps 3 and 4 five more times. Leave similar-sized gaps between the lines.

6

Fill in the small square in the top corner with a black felt-tip pen. Then fill in every other row.

7 Use a pencil to shade the white spaces, to the right of the diagonal line. They should be less and less dark the further they are from the black square.

Keep your pencil at the same angle as the diagonal line.

←-- Press your pencil firmly...

←-- ...less firmly...

←-- ...and lightly.

8 Turn your picture around and look at it from the side.

The illusion works even better if you take a photo of it from this angle.

CREATE YOUR OWN COMIC STRIP

Find some paper and follow these tips to help you draw and write your own comics.

Comic strips combine pictures and speech bubble to tell stories.

The scenes are usually arranged into boxes called panels. Panels can vary in size and shape to suit each scene. You read the panels from left to right.

CAPTION BOXES SET THE SCENE:
YESTERDAY, IN **NEVER GET BORED** HQ

THIS IS A SPEECH BUBBLE.

THIS IS A THOUGHT BUBBLE.

Comic

SOMEONE WITH A LOT TO SAY MIGHT NEED TWO LINKED BUBBLES.

PLEASE TICKLE MY TUMMY, HUMAN.

NOT NOW, CAT. I'M BUSY.

Comic

Words for noises, or sound effects, are often written directly on top of the panel.

PARTS OF THE PICTURE CAN EXTEND, OR FALL OUT OF **THE PANELS.**

KAPLONK!

CHARACTER BUILDING

YOU'LL NEED A CHARACTER (OR CHARACTERS) TO STAR IN YOUR COMIC. YOU COULD START WITH A STICK FIGURE, THEN ADD MORE DETAILS.

ANYTHING CAN BECOME A CHARACTER IF YOU GIVE IT A FACE - EVEN AN EVERYDAY OBJECT SUCH AS A BOOK OR A MUG.

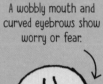

KEEP YOUR CHARACTERS SIMPLE BECAUSE YOU'LL NEED TO DRAW THEM OVER AND OVER AGAIN.

WITH SIMPLE LINES AND DOTS, YOU CAN GIVE YOUR CHARACTERS FACES THAT SHOW DIFFERENT EMOTIONS.

Wide eyes show fear or surprise.

Eyebrows that slope down can show your character is angry...

...or up to no good.

A wobbly mouth and curved eyebrows show worry or fear.

PLAN IT OUT

First, decide what your comic is going to be about and what needs to go in each panel.

Write notes about what each scene will show. Specify any captions, speech or thought bubbles and sound effects you want to include.

Panel 1
Description - a close up of Finn asleep.
Thought bubble - shows him dreaming about an incredible ice-cream sundae.

Panel 2
Description - show that Finn has fallen asleep at his desk at school.
Sound effects - snoring

Don't try to squeeze too much into each panel.

STUCK FOR IDEAS?

You could make a comic about...

...an octopus who knits.

...a dog that travels back in time to ancient Egypt.

...an alien on the run from the police.

...a story you know well, such as a fairy tale.

DOODLE PATTERNS

You could fill a piece of paper with several different patterns or choose just one of these ideas.

Draw big spots, then turn each one into a flower by drawing on petals.

Combine spots, squiggles and lines, both straight and curved.

Keep your pen on the paper for as long as possible to make this maze pattern.

Doodle overlapping circles... ...and fill them in with different patterns.

Join spots together with straight, black lines.

Add lots and lots of dots inside a circle.

Draw big triangles side by side. Doodle a different pattern inside each one.

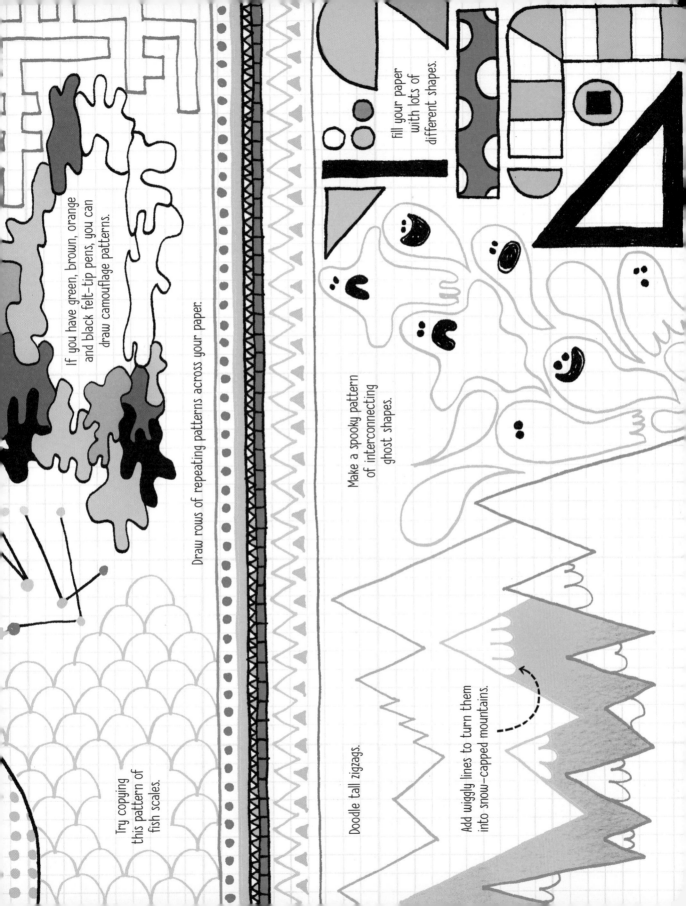

If you have green, brown, orange and black felt-tip pens, you can draw camouflage patterns.

Draw rows of repeating patterns across your paper.

Try copying this pattern of fish scales.

fill your paper with lots of different shapes.

Make a spooky pattern of interconnecting ghost shapes.

Doodle tall zigzags.

Add wiggly lines to turn them into snow-capped mountains.

DESIGN A FASHION COLLECTION

Fashion designers sketch and doodle their ideas as they come up with a new collection of outfits each season. Why not try to design your own?

Make a "mood board"

Start by bringing together your ideas on a big piece of paper...

Decide a theme for your collection.

Coral reef chic

Empress Angelfish

Anemone pink

Pop of yellow

Choose similar or contrasting shades for the clothes.

Sunlit wave

Hot crab

Deep sea blue

Doodle patterns that you want to use.

Think about different shapes that you could use when designing your clothes.

Coral-fringed sleeves

Octopus skirt

Fish-shaped accessories

Look in old magazines or newspapers for pictures connected with your theme.

Wave top

Bubbles

SAVE THE CORAL REEFS

You could cut them out and stick them on your mood board too.

Sketch your ideas for individual elements or describe them in words.

Now, get designing...

Use the ideas on your own mood board (or the mood board on page 42) and copy the shapes on this page to sketch clothes and accessories for your collection.

European sailors used to wear straw hats with a flat top and brim. They became known as "boaters."

HATS

After drawing this mannequin head shape, you could copy one of the hat designs or make up your own. Decorate them to match your theme.

Baseball cap

Coral logo

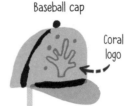

T-SHIRTS

Copy the shape below, then customize designs for T-shirts with pictures, patterns or slogans.

Beret

Homburg

OUTFITS

If you place a thin piece of paper over the body shape on the right, you could draw an entire outfit on top. Use the shape to help you to get the proportions right.

You can create lots of outfits in this way.

ACCESSORIES

Design accessories to complete the look.

Snorkel sunglasses

Starfish earrings

fish backpack

Sharkfin shoes

PAINT OUTDOORS

You don't have to stay indoors to paint. So pack up your paints, paintbrushes and a pad of paper, then step outside. Don't forget to take a jar filled with water too – you'll need it to clean your brushes.

SETTING UP

First, find somewhere you can paint comfortably. Try standing up with a clipboard or rest a pad of paper on your knees.

Make sure you can see at least a few things that you'd like to try painting – far away or close at hand.

PAINTING TIPS

Here are some ideas for you to try as you paint...

Paint quickly, using simple shapes and lines, for people or animals on the move.

If you can see a row of rooftops, you could paint a line to show their different shapes.

Paintings don't have to be realistic. For instance, you could paint any patterns you see in water ripples instead.

Make several small paintings on the same piece of paper to record some of the things in view.

These types of pictures are called studies.

You could make the easel on page 22 and set it up outdoors.

PERFECT VIEWS

To help you choose the view you're going to paint, you could use a simple tool called a viewfinder. You can make one with a piece of paper.

1

fold a piece of paper in half, this way.

2

Cut a small square out of both sides, along the fold.

3

Open the paper. Hold it up in front of you with both hands and look through the hole.

It's easier to look through the viewfinder with one eye only. Close your other eye to help you to focus.

EMBRACE THE ELEMENTS

Here are some more outdoor painting activities for you to try, whatever the weather.

On a warm, dry day, use a clean paintbrush and some water to draw pictures on a wooden fence or stone slabs.

If you wait long enough, you'll see your pictures fade in the sun.

If it's raining, you could paint a pattern of shapes on a piece of paper, BEFORE you go outside...

Then, leave it in the rain, with the painted side facing up.

You could stand under an umbrella to watch how the raindrops change the pattern.

45

TURN OBJECTS INTO PICTURES

You can make pictures by arranging different objects on a piece of paper and drawing details next to them. These types of pictures look best when you look at them from directly above.

1

First, find the objects you want to transform. You could look for some of the things shown on these pages, or come up with your own ideas.

2

Place the objects on paper. Then, hold down each item firmly, with your opposite hand, as you draw.

3

You could take photos of the pictures you've made before you put the objects back.

TAPE OR SNAIL?

A roll of tape makes a snail's shell.

PAPERCLIP PARTY

Draw faces, arms and legs to turn each paperclip into someone dancing.

GOOD SHIP GARLIC

Draw a line for a mast and triangles for sails.

BUTTON WHEELS

You'll need two buttons: one for the front and one for the back.

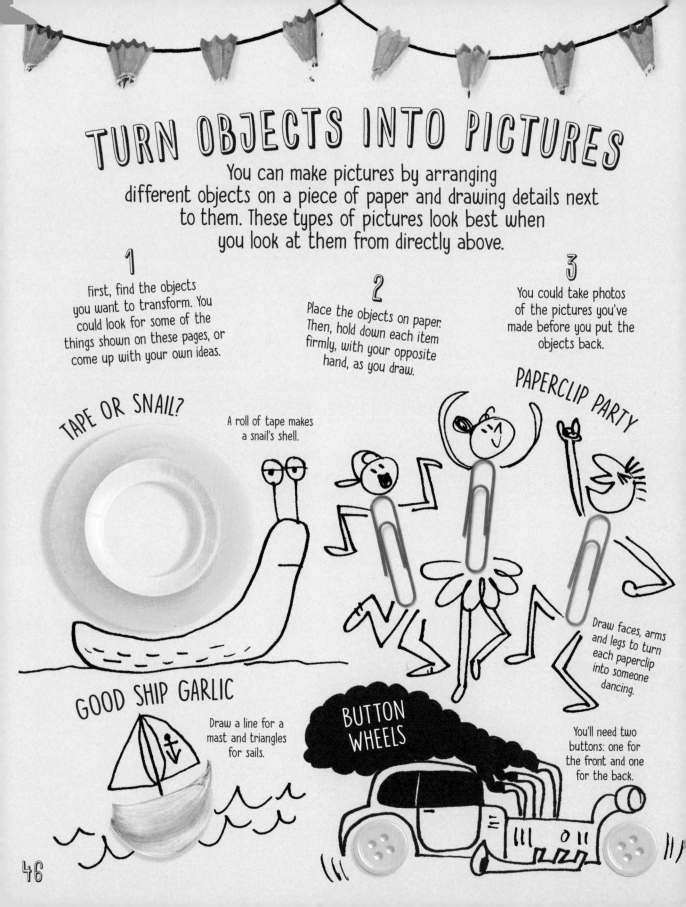

UP IN THE AIR

Maybe you could use the lid from a bottle for a hot-air balloon?

How about pieces of dried macaroni for parachutes?

ROBO SHARPENER

Imagine that a pencil sharpener is a robot's face... You just need to add some antennae and its body.

KEY CROC

If you can find a key shaped like a crocodile's upper jaw, you could draw the rest of the crocodile around it.

SAVE THE SHAVINGS

Collect shavings every time you sharpen your pencils. Then, make pictures with them too.

Short shavings could be flames from a rocket.

Long shavings are good for a lion's mane.

You could use glue to stick the shavings to the paper when you're satisfied with their positions.

47

PICK YOUR PAINTS

You can use the diagram below to find out how to mix different paints together – and how to choose the most suitable colors for your pictures.

The **BLUE ARROWS** point to the colors you can make when you mix two colors of paint together.

Colors opposite each other along the **ORANGE LINES** are known as complementary. They look zingy and bright together.

You can also make brown by mixing red, yellow and blue.

BROWN

If you want to make a paler color, just mix in some white.

WHITE

Add tiny amounts of black paint to create darker colors.

BLACK

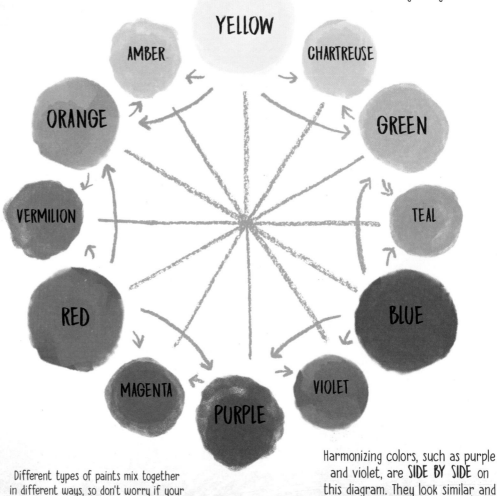

YELLOW

AMBER

CHARTREUSE

ORANGE

GREEN

VERMILION

TEAL

RED

BLUE

MAGENTA

VIOLET

PURPLE

Different types of paints mix together in different ways, so don't worry if your paints don't match these spots exactly.

Harmonizing colors, such as purple and violet, are **SIDE BY SIDE** on this diagram. They look similar and blend together in pictures.

COUNTLESS COLORS

Create lots more colors by varying the amounts of paints you mix. For instance, you could use your paints to see how many shades of yellow, purple or green you can make...

Rotten banana – 4 parts yellow to 2 parts brown, plus a tiny amount of black

Faded lavender – Equal amounts of red, blue and white

If you like any of your colors (and want to mix them again), you could make up a name for each one and write down its "recipe."

Toothpaste green – 1 dollop of green, 2 small squirts of blue and 1 drop of white, mixed together

SPECIAL EFFECTS

You could pick pairs of complementary colors from the diagram on page 48 to make eye-catching pictures.

For instance, if you're painting a green parrot and you want it to stand out, you should paint the background red.

If you want to give your paintings a sense of calm, you should use harmonizing colors.

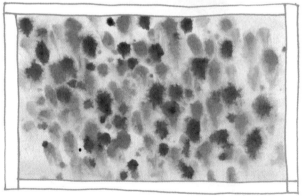

Purple aliens look most striking on a yellow planet.

You could fill a piece of paper with splotches of blue and teal paints.

WHAT DO THEY MEAN?

Like many artists before you, you could use red, yellow or blue in your pictures to suggest meanings, traditionally associated with these colors...

RED
Heat or anger

YELLOW
Sunshine or happiness

BLUE
Coolness or sadness

49

MAKE SHADOW ART

You can use light from a lamp or the sun to make shadow pictures indoors and outdoors.

INDOORS

1 Turn off any other lights nearby, then shine a lamp on a piece of paper.

2 Arrange different items on the paper, so they cast shadows.

3 Draw details on the paper to turn the shadow shapes into pictures.

You can move the lamp – or the items – to adjust the shapes and sizes of the shadows.

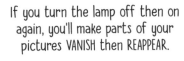

If you turn the lamp off then on again, you'll make parts of your pictures VANISH then REAPPEAR.

OUTDOORS

1 On a bright, sunny day, stand on a hard surface outside.

Strike any pose you like, but try to keep still.

2 Ask a friend to draw around the edge of your shadow in chalk.

You could use different colored chalks to fill in the shape.

Try making shadows on a sandy beach too.

Draw in the sand, around the edges of the shadow, with a stick or stone.

SPLATTER PAINT

Save your old toothbrush, next time it needs replacing, so you can use it to splatter paint onto pictures. Go outdoors and put lots of newspaper under your paper before you begin, to avoid making a mess.

1 Dip the bristles of the toothbrush in some paint.

2 Hold the toothbrush above a piece of paper. Use one of the fingers on your other hand to flick the bristles. This splatters the paint.

3 Repeat the steps to add more layers of splattered paint. You could use several colors on the same picture.

DRIP PAINT

Load a paintbrush with paint and shake it above your picture to add bigger drops of paint.

SHAPES

1 Cut out different shapes from thick paper or cardboard. Put them on the paper to keep paint off parts of your picture.

2 Then, get splattering.

You could remove one of the shapes, and then splatter different colored paints.

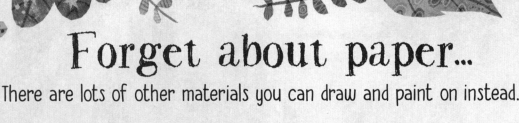

Forget about paper...

There are lots of other materials you can draw and paint on instead.

LEAVES

Collect leaves that have fallen to the ground. Then, decorate them with permanent markers or paints. Handle the leaves gently, so you don't crush them.

Rings within rings

You could paint these patterns on lots of leaves, then arrange them into a snake.

faces

FOIL

If an old piece of kitchen foil is clean enough to reuse, you could try painting on it with poster paints. Lay the foil flat or wrap it around a board before you paint.

Your brushstrokes will glide across the foil's surface.

Try making a picture of some cog shapes...

...or a robot.

GLASS JAR

Brighten up an old glass jar with some paints, then use it to store things such as pens and pencils.

1

Wash and scrub the jar with warm water and dishwashing liquid to remove any labels.

2

Then, dry the jar before pouring a small amount of liquid paint inside.

3

Tilt and shake the jar gently, to swirl the paint up its sides.

4

You could repeat steps 2 and 3 with different colors.

5

Put the lid on the jar and leave it upside down. The paint will drip and make a pattern before it dries.

To recycle the jar later, you should wash the paint off first.

SHOEBOX CANVAS

Some artists paint on a type of fabric called canvas, stretched across chunky wooden frames. These are known as box canvases.

You could paint in a similar way on the lid of a shoebox.

1 Put the lid on top of some sheets of old newspaper. Then cover it with a layer of paint for a background.

Remember to paint the sides too.

2 When the background layer is dry, paint your picture on top, like this sunflower.

And instead of pens...

You could "draw" with pebbles — or dried foods such as rice, lentils or beans.

Use a pencil to draw a spiral on a piece of paper, then arrange pebbles along the line.

How about drawing the outline of an animal, such as this beetle or panda?

Then fill in the sections with different types of rice, beans and lentils.

Lentils

Kidney beans

Rice

Black beans

Don't leave any gaps.

DISCOVER SHADING

There are lots of techniques for shading with a pencil.
If you look at the picture below and read the captions,
you'll find different ways you can shade.

Simple shading

Hold a pencil at an angle and move it over your paper, to shade an area, like this...

Hatching

Fill a shape with lots of diagonal lines. They should be quite straight and the spaces between the lines should be roughly the same.

Stippling

Draw lots of little dots. The picture will look darker if lots of dots are close together.

This bush looks lighter because the lines have bigger gaps between them.

Blending

Use your fingers to smudge pencil markings so they look smoother.

Cross-hatching

Draw diagonal lines in one direction. Then add more lines over them in a different direction.

Scumbling

Doodle lots of continuous squiggles.

TOP SECRET

Shade in spies

Try the different shading techniques by drawing your own spies.

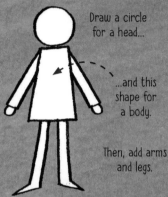

Draw a circle for a head...

...and this shape for a body.

Then, add arms and legs.

Conceal each spy's identity with...

...a hat...

...sunglasses...

...and a jacket.

Or...

...cover part of a spy's face with a mask.

Then, decide how to shade them in.

Shady sides

Shading can help you to show the direction of a light source, such as a lamp or the sun, in your pictures. Shade parts of your picture that are outside the range of the light, so they look dark.

From below

CAUGHT YOU!

From above

From the side

Shine a light

When it's dark, shine a light on a ball or another small object. If you move the light, you can change how much of the ball appears in light or shade.

This works best if you turn off the other lights in the room.

You could draw a circle and shade part of it in to show how much of the ball isn't lit up.

55

DRAW WITH WORDS

A hundred years ago, a french poet named Guillaume Apollinaire wrote poems in the shapes of a dove, a palm tree, the Eiffel Tower and other things. You could turn words into pictures by making shapes as you write.

1

First, use a pencil to draw all the things you want to include in your picture.

You can also draw lines – straight or wiggly – as guides for you to write on.

2

Then write lots of words inside the shapes or along the lines with a pen. Try to write words ASSOCIATED with your picture.

3

Wait for the ink to dry then erase the pencil markings.

You could write one letter again and again to create a shape...

SEA AIR EAST BLOW FLAPGUST SAIL AHOY SAIL SEA SPEED FURL CANVAS CATCH THE WIND FLY SAIL GUST SKIM SPEED FLURRY NAVIGATE BLOW SAIL AIR NORTH BILLOW BREEZY WIND BOB CROSS JOURNEY EASY NORTH AHOY BLAST SAIL GUST PUFF CANVAS SAILAWAY NAVIGATE LURCH flutter flutter flit flit flit flutter flap flap flap flap flap flap SHIPSHAPE BLOW MAST MAST MAST MAST MAST MAST MAST FILL BLOW ALONG

STERN BOAT AHOY NIMBLE FLOAT RIDE WATERPROOF FAST TRUSTY BOAT SEAWORTHY FLOAT FLOAT BOW THE WAVES AHOY WATERPROOF SEA SEA TRUSTY BOAT SKIM FLOATING SEAWORTHY NIMBLE FLOAT crest fall roll tilt swell rise rise peak crest tilt swell rise rise rise peak crest again rise rise rise peak cre

Calm quiet soft bobbing sea smooth ripples waves swell rise rise rise cre

0000000000000...

COTTON DARK GLOOMY DARK BLACK CLOUDY COTTON WOOL CLUMPS OF RAINY WATERY GLOOMY COTTON WOOLLY CLUMPS OF RAINY WATERY COTTON
COTTON DARK GENTLY BLACK SOFT RAINBALL DRIFTING COTTON
MISTY SKY RAINBALL FLOATING FLUFFY CLOUDY
FLUFFY BURST WOOLLY DRIFTING MISTY SKY
RAINBALL MISTY GLOOMY DARK BLACK
WATERY CLOUDY SOFT WATERY COTTON
WOOLLY SHEEP SKY PUFFS WET MISTY GLOOMY DARK
WATERY SKY SPLODGE MIST GLOOMY BILLOWING MISTY FLUFFBALLS OF

A TOWER, SET IN OR NEAR THE

SEA, WITH A FLASHING LIGHT THAT

GUIDES SHIPS OR WARNS THEM OF DANGER.

Look up words in a thesaurus to find words with similar meanings. Include them in the same parts of your picture.

raindrip drops
splat spit splash
spplish splosh
drizzle down
drop drip

Using a dictionary, search for the definition of something you want to draw – like this lighthouse. Then, write out the definition as part of your picture.

You can vary the size of your words and letters as you write.

You could draw on some extra details, like these orange stripes.

CRAGGY GNARLY TREACHEROUS ROCKY ROCKS STEEP HIGH CLIMBING CLIFFS CLIFFS

rise big wave Crest fall flow tilt swell rise rise crest break fall fall tilt swell rise rise rise rise rise rise peak fall

NOW... choose words to make an erupting volcano.

EXPLODE BURST
LAVA BOOM LAVA BUBBLY BANG
ERUPTED
HOT VOLCANO BURN
ROCK MAGMA HOTTEST FIRE

Here the letter O has been used to draw an octopus.

57

PUT PICTURES INTO PERSPECTIVE

If you're drawing a landscape or scene, you can use a trick called perspective to make it look more like the way your eyes see the world. Just remember this rule: the further away something is, the smaller it should appear in your picture.

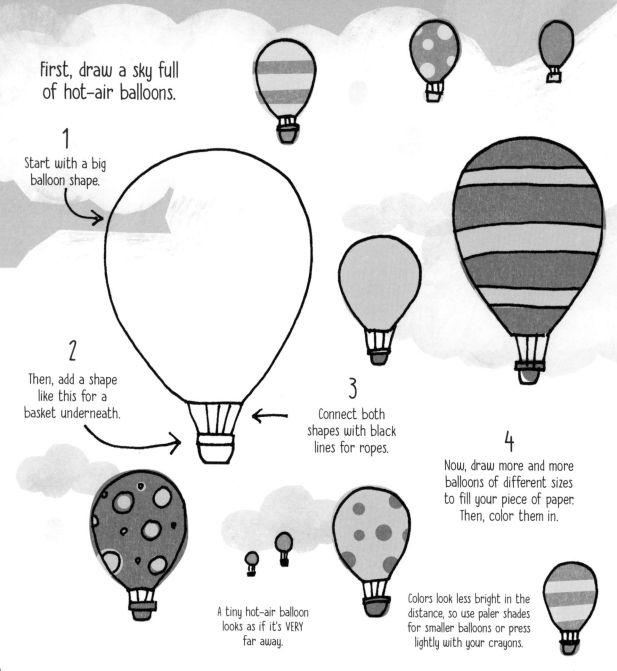

First, draw a sky full of hot-air balloons.

1

Start with a big balloon shape.

2

Then, add a shape like this for a basket underneath.

3

Connect both shapes with black lines for ropes.

4

Now, draw more and more balloons of different sizes to fill your piece of paper. Then, color them in.

A tiny hot-air balloon looks as if it's VERY far away.

Colors look less bright in the distance, so use paler shades for smaller balloons or press lightly with your crayons.

Then, show two stick people throwing a ball.

1 Draw a big stick person in the bottom left corner of your paper, like this.

2 Use a bright green pen, to add a curved line behind for a hill. Color it in.

3 Draw a hill in the background in pale green. Add a smaller stick person on this hill.

4 Next, draw a ball near the small stick person. You could add some lines to make it look as if it's moving away from the big person.

Now... play tricks with perspective.

You could draw things

SMALLER or **BIGGER**

than they ought to look — according to the rules of perspective — to make funny pictures...

Make a small object look huge by drawing people climbing over it.

How about a VERY small cat in front of a VERY big mouse?

Sketch a giant chicken behind several rows of skyscrapers.

I'm the HUGEST hen in the world.

DRAW AND PAINT BACK IN TIME

Imagine that you've just climbed aboard this "Never Get Bored" time machine with all your drawing and painting materials. Now get ready to explore the art of the past...

NEVER GET BORED TIME MACHINE

FIRST STOP: CHINA
800 YEARS AGO

Artists in China used paintbrushes and black ink to draw pictures, like the ones below, on paper or silk. They captured how things looked with just a few lines.

Try making a picture in this style using a paintbrush and watered-down black paint instead of ink.

Try copying this tower. It's called a pagoda.

Draw wiggly lines for mountains in the distance. Doodle trees along the top.

The loose effect of these types of drawings works best if you hold your brush at the top of its handle, in an upright position.

To paint bamboo, draw thick and thin lines for stalks, then add lots of leaves.

Try drawing cats in different poses. Cats often appear in Chinese art.

SECOND STOP: ANCIENT GREECE
2,500 YEARS AGO

Ancient Greek artists made beautiful reddish-brown pots, which they decorated with black paint. Follow these steps to create your own pot designs.

1

Draw a large pot shape in pencil on a piece of paper. Fill in the shape with reddish-brown paint.

You could copy one of these traditional Greek shapes.

2

Once the paint has dried, use a pencil to draw pictures and patterns on top. Here are some ideas...

Monsters

Fish

3

When you're satisfied with your design, go over it in black paint or pen. Then, cut out the pot shape.

Rows of patterns

LAST STOP: ANCIENT EGYPT
4,000 YEARS AGO

Here you'll discover how to draw three symbols often found in ancient Egyptian art.

Green, yellow, blue and red each had different meanings to the Egyptians, too.

CROOK AND FLAIL

These farming tools represented the power of Egyptian rulers, known as pharaohs.

Flail
Crook

GREEN was a symbol of growth and goodness.

SCARAB BEETLE

This beetle was meant to bring good luck.

YELLOW meant the sun and eternity.

BLUE stood for birth and life.

EYE OF HORUS

This eye was a symbol of safety and good health.

RED could stand for energy or destruction.

DRAW ON A STEAMED-UP WINDOW

Windows and mirrors steam up when there's lots of warm, damp air around them. See this happen after a hot shower or if you're in a car on a cold day.

Next time you see a window or mirror that's steamed-up, you could use your hands to make pictures.

Baby steps

Press the bottom of your fist against steamed-up glass to make a little "footprint."

Then add "toeprints" with your fingers.

Use your other fist to make the other foot.

Crying eyes?

If you draw an eye then wait...

...your picture might drip "tears."

Stick figures

Draw a thick line with your finger.

Add a shape for a head...

Use your fingernails to add flyaway, wispy hairs.

...bulges for arms...

...and two little lines for legs.

What other pictures can you draw?

Mysterious messages

You could write words with your finger too.

Oil from your skin leaves invisible marks. So remember to clean the window or mirror when you've finished.

Try adding a squiggly shadow with the tip of a finger.

HELLO THERE

If you don't clean the glass, your pictures or messages will reappear next time it steams up.

BUILD A CITY

You can use poster paints to transform boxes
into buildings for your own mini city.

1
Collect cardboard boxes
and cartons of different
shapes and sizes.

2
Paint the top and sides
of some of them with
a large brush.

3
When the paint has dried, add
window shapes with black paint.
Wait for them to dry too.

NOW...

Arrange the buildings into a cityscape...

The windows could be
squares, rectangles,
triangles or circles.

You could add
a helipad.

Draw windows
on the boxes
you haven't
painted, using a
felt-tip pen.

Stack the
boxes on top
of each other.

If you want to make a grid of roads for toy
cars, you could join together pieces of black
paper with tape. Then, paint some white
stripes down the middle, like this.

SPRINKLE SALT ON PAINT

Just a sprinkling of salt can have an unusual effect on watery paint. Find some salt and follow the steps below to paint pictures of starry skies and distant planets.

SPRINKLED STARS

1

Brush lots of watery paint over a piece of very thick paper.

Cover the paper with paint as fast as you can.

Thick paper works best because it doesn't absorb the paint too quickly.

2

Right away while the paint is still very wet, sprinkle some salt on top. Then, leave it to dry.

3

When the paint is dry, you can brush off any loose salt with your fingers.

What happens?

The salt absorbs some of the water from the paint. This leaves a star-like pattern behind.

64

SALTY PLANETS

Now use some more salt, paints and glue to add textured planets to your picture.

1

Draw a circle for a planet.

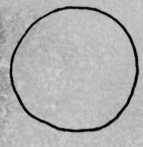

2

Then, spread some glue inside the outline.

3

Sprinkle lots of salt on top to cover the glue. Wait for it to dry.

4

Shake the paper gently to remove any loose salt.

5

Dip a paintbrush into some paint and dab it on the salt. Watch the paint spread across the salt.

You could doodle stars in the background – or add some aliens. Draw them on another piece of paper. Then, cut them out and stick them on.

6

Keep dabbing more paint on the salt. See what happens if you add spots in a different color, too. Then, leave your picture to dry.

DRAW UNICORNS

Follow the steps below to draw unicorns, narwhals and MORE one-horned creatures.

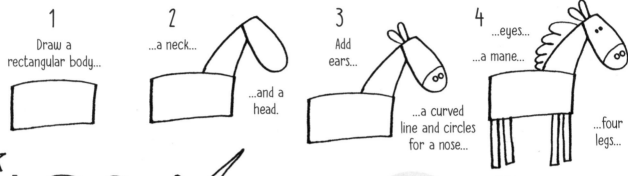

1 Draw a rectangular body...

2 ...a neck... ...and a head.

3 Add ears... ...a curved line and circles for a nose...

4 ...eyes... ...a mane... ...four legs...

5 ...a swishy tail... ...and, of course, a horn!

Add wings, if you like.

ALL ABOUT UNICORNS

Unicorn means "one horn" in Latin.

The earliest drawings of unicorns are cave paintings in Lascaux, France. They were made more than 17,000 years ago.

In some myths, unicorns have magical powers, such as the ability to cure people when they're ill.

Horns aplenty

Try varying the horns you draw to make your unicorns different from each other.

Add curved lines for a twisted horn.

My horn only started growing last week.

A unicorn's horn doesn't have to be white...

Draw an "ice-cream cone" horn for a horse that's pretending to be a unicorn.

Narwhals

Unicorns may only exist in pictures and stories, but in seas around the world there really are one-horned creatures called narwhals. They're sometimes known as "unicorns of the sea."

1 Draw a shape like this...

2 Add two tail fins...

...two flippers...

3 ...a horn... ...an eye...

...a wide mouth...

4 ...lines to the horn.... ...and speckles.

A narwhal "horn" is actually a tusk – a long tooth.

NOW...

...transform all manner of animals into uni-beasts by giving them fabulous horns.

You could copy these pictures, or make up your own.

UNIBAT

UNICAT

Sometimes Unicat Floof's horn gets in her way – for instance, when she's trying to curl up on someone's lap.

Invent names and descriptions for your uni-beasts, and write them on your pictures.

UNIPANDA

UNISNAKE

UNICROC

Harry the Unicroc dreams of flying.

67

SOLVE PICTURE PUZZLES

You'll need a pencil or pen and some paper to help you find the solutions to these puzzles. All the answers are at the back of the book.

NON-STOP DRAWING

Can you draw each of these pictures without stopping? You mustn't lift your pen or pencil from the paper or go over the same line twice.

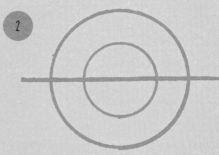

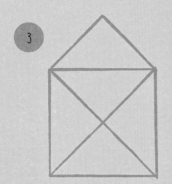

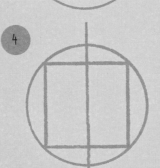

ROOFTOPS

Imagine that you are in a plane flying over these three groups of buildings. Which group matches each of the bird's-eye views on the right?

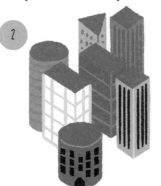

BIRD'S-EYE VIEWS

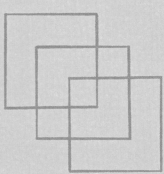

68 NOW, draw a picture of the view that's missing.

FROM TWO TO FOUR

Where should two caterpillars wiggle to make four triangles? Copy the six caterpillars onto a piece of paper, repositioning just two of them, to show where they need to go.

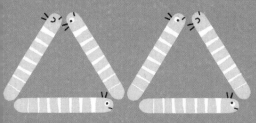

FAST FOX

How quickly can you draw this fox shape, using just five triangles?

SHEEP PEN PUZZLE

First, copy these three rows of sheep onto your paper. Make sure they line up. Now, draw only three squares to separate the sheep into different pens.

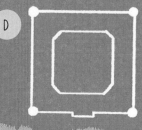

You could draw dots instead of sheep.

FAMOUS FLOORPLANS

Architects draw floorplans to show the shape, size, parts and rooms of a building as seen from above. Can you match each of these floorplans to the buildings below?

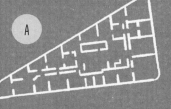

A

B

C

D

3 Flatiron Building, New York, USA

2 Taj Mahal, Agra, India

1 St. Basil's Cathedral, Moscow, Russia

4 The Great Mosque, Djenné, Mali

69

MAKE MONOPRINTS

Printing blocks let you print similar images again and again. But you can also make a print with paint that's a complete one-off. It's called a MONOPRINT.

FIRST, YOU'LL NEED TO MAKE A "PRINTING PLATE"...

1 Cut out a rectangle from a piece of cardboard.

It should be about half the size of this page.

2 Then, cut a piece of foil, big enough to wrap around the cardboard.

Tape the edges down on the back.

THEN, PAINT AND PRINT...

1 Cover the top of the plate with a layer of paint.

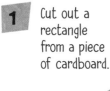

The paint shouldn't be too watery or too thick.

Don't worry about being neat, but make sure the paint covers all the edges.

2 While the paint is wet, use a dry brush, stick or your finger to draw patterns in it.

This removes some of the paint from the plate.

Lines

Shapes

Scales

3 Next, press the plate, paint-side down, onto a piece of paper.

Press down firmly and evenly, but don't move the plate from side to side.

4 Carefully lift off the plate to reveal your monoprint.

VOILA! WOW! It's totally ORIGINAL!

DIFFERENT MARKS

Try making different marks in the paint for your next print. Remember to press down gently, so you don't rip the foil.

You can use your printing plate again and again. Wipe it clean with an old cloth or wait for the paint to dry before you cover it with a new layer of paint...

Fat splotches with your thumb

Spots with your little finger

Thin lines with the "wrong" end of your paintbrush

Starbursts

BEYOND BRUSHES

You could draw into the paint with the prongs of a fork or an old toothbrush, VERY carefully...

...or WIPE shapes and marks with cotton balls or scrunched-up tissue.

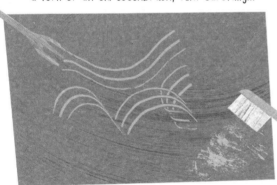

PAINT ON PAINT

 1 Paint several different colored stripes, next to each other, across your plate.

2 Then, paint a picture or pattern on top with another color before making a print.

WATCH OUT! If you take too long, the paint will dry.

DRAW IN UNUSUAL WAYS

Surprise your pens and pencils with these
unexpected drawing techniques.

THE WRONG HAND

You could draw patterns and shapes
with the hand you don't usually use.
Here are some ideas to try...

How neatly can you draw the shape of
a heart or star with your other hand?
Try again and again.

TALENTED TOES

To draw with one of your feet...

...place a felt-tip pen between your
big toe and the toe next to it.

Grip the pen with these toes,
then draw lines or squiggles
across a piece of paper
on the floor.

CLOSE YOUR EYES

First, draw this picture
of a fly-eating flower
on a piece of paper.

Now, close your eyes
and draw the same
flower from memory.

Compare your pictures.
How different do they look?

Is it an
owl?

A fish?

You could try drawing
other things with your
eyes closed, too.

Maybe you could challenge
your friends to guess what
you're drawing?

TWO PENCILS ARE BETTER THAN ONE

Hold two pencils or pens next to each other and draw with them both at the same time.

You could use some tape to secure each bundle. Make sure the tips of the pens or pencils line up.

Try this technique with more pens or pencils in each bundle.

Drawing in this way adds a sense of movement to your pictures.

DROP DOTS

Grip a felt-tip pen lightly and hold it just above a piece of paper. Then, bounce the nib on the paper to cover it with tiny dots.

THICK LINES

First, sharpen a pencil. It needs a long point.

Then, hold the pencil so it's almost on its side, and rub its tip across the paper.

You could make wavy rows of short lines...

...or draw a lion's face and mane.

DRAW WITH SHAPES

What kinds of pictures of animals can you make by drawing only triangles, squares or circles?

PAINT WITH BUBBLES

Make pictures by blowing lots of colorful bubbles. All you need is paint, water, dishwashing liquid, paper and a paper straw.

1

First, lay out a piece of newspaper or scrap paper, in case things get messy.

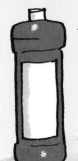

Then, squirt some liquid paint into an old yogurt container.

Add a squirt of dishwashing liquid...

...and a splash of warm water, too.

2

Stir the mixture with the straw, then blow through it until bubbles rise above the top of the container.

If bubbles don't form, try adding more water and dishwashing liquid.

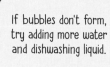

3

Now make your picture. Place a piece of paper over the bubbles and lift it off.

You could use the straw to scrape off the bubbles instead.

4

Make more bubbles to add to your picture in the same way. You could use different colors, too.

Turn your bubbly picture into an underwater scene...

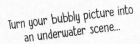

Doodle some sea creatures with a black pen.

TURN ONE COLOR INTO MANY

Even if you're only using one color, you can still make
lots of shades. Just mix it with different amounts of water.

First try to make as many shades as you can...

Paint a small spot with
some liquid paint.

Add a few drops of water to the paint,
then paint another spot alongside.

Keep mixing more water with the paint
and painting spots until they vanish
into the paper.

If you have one green paint, you could mix five shades with different
amounts of water to create a leafy jungle scene.

1

Start by covering
your paper with
the lightest green
you mixed. Then
wait for it to dry.

3

Then paint a row
of darker trees in
the foreground and
some shapes for
bushes too.

5

Paint a few more
leaves with your
darkest green. You
could add a flying
bird if you like.

2

Add some tree
shapes in the
background in a
slightly darker
green.

4

Use an even darker
shade for leaves
and vines coming in
from the sides of
the paper.

Decorate any leaves
you painted in step
4 with spots and
lines, using the
darkest shade.

75

MAKE INVISIBLE INKS

There are a few types of liquids that you can use as invisible inks.
Any pictures you draw with them will disappear when they dry. BUT you can make
them reappear when you know the trick at the bottom of this page.

INVISIBLE INKS TO TRY

Lemon Juice
Squeeze the juice from a lemon into a jar.

Milk
Vinegar
Add a few spoonfuls of either into a different cup.

1

Choose one of the "inks" from the suggestions on the left. Then, use a paintbrush to draw a picture on white paper.

2 Keep dipping your brush in the "ink" as you draw. Then leave your picture to dry until it has vanished.

Now, use heat to reveal the paper's secrets. You could...

Hold a hair dryer near your picture to warm it...

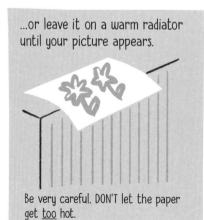

As the dry "ink" on the paper is heated, it reacts with the air and turns brown.

...or leave it on a warm radiator until your picture appears.

Be very careful. DON'T let the paper get <u>too</u> hot.

If it's hot and sunny, you could leave the paper outdoors to heat up.

TRANSFORMING PICTURES

First, draw things with a pen. Then, draw over them with invisible ink, to make pictures that change when they're heated. Use these ideas to inspire you.

Transform a horse, drawn in pen...

...into a zebra with "invisible" stripes.

Put a monster...

...behind bars.

Is it a slug?

No! It's a snail.

Watch out, cow!

There's a UFO behind you.

CATCH FISH!

1

Draw waves on a piece of paper with a blue pen or pencil.

2

Then, use one of the invisible inks and a brush to add the shapes of ten fish. Wait for the ink to dry.

3

Now, challenge a friend to catch as many of the hidden fish as possible by drawing around a cup, anywhere on the paper, three times.

4

Reveal where the fish are by heating the paper. You win if your friend only caught four fish or fewer.

PAINT BLUE AND WHITE PLATES

For hundreds of years, potters in Asia and Europe have made white plates with blue pictures and patterns. Maybe their ideas could inspire you to decorate paper plates?

WHY BLUE?

Pottery is made at very high temperatures, and only a few paints can withstand this heat. One of the paints that can – cobalt blue – is made with a bluish substance called cobalt oxide.

Potters make a plate from white clay, then paint it with cobalt blue.

The paint looks dark blue at first.

Next, they dip the plate in a varnish-like liquid, known as glaze.

Finally, they bake the plate for several hours in a special, very hot oven, called a kiln.

The clay hardens in the oven and the dark blue turns bright and shiny.

HOW TO MAKE A PLATE

You could reuse old paper plates, wiped clean for this activity, but it's easy to draw and cut out plate shapes instead...

1 Place a kitchen plate topside down on a piece of thick white paper. Draw around it.

2 Place a smaller plate or bowl in the middle and draw around it with a pencil, to suggest a rim.

3 Cut out the plate, around the big circle.

DELFT DESIGNS

The windmill picture on the left is typical of a type of pottery, known as Delftware. It's named after the Dutch city of Delft, where potters started making blue and white plates, vases and tiles over 400 years ago.

HOW TO DECORATE IT

There are different ideas for decorations on this page, based on Chinese pottery.
You could copy one of the patterns around the edge of your plate, then draw
a fish, or birds around a tree, or a dragon in the middle.

You can use blue paints,
inks or food dye and
a brush if you want
to paint...

...or blue pencils
or felt-tip pens
if you prefer
to draw.

In Chinese art,
dragons traditionally
have five claws on
each foot.

Types of fish called koi carp
often appear in Japanese and
Chinese art.

Paint or draw
"C" shapes for
scales.

Don't forget
its "whiskers."
They're called
barbels.

Add water lily leaf
shapes like these...

Include squiggles
to suggest ripples
of water.

Draw shapes or
doodle wavy lines
for flying birds.

Paint a trunk
and dangling
branches for
a weeping
willow tree.

BRILLIANT BLUES

ULTRAMARINE

Lapis lazuli (a type of
semi-precious gemstone)
used to be ground
into a powder to make
ultramarine paint.

INDIGO

This blue dye was originally made
from the leaves of a type of bean
plant. It's used to dye jeans and
clothes made from denim.

In 2009, scientists discovered a
new type of blue pigment that
doesn't fade. They called it...

YInMn BLUE

...after the symbols of the chemical
elements it contains: yttrium (Y),
indium (In) and manganese (Mn).

79

FRAME YOUR ARTWORKS

Make eye-catching picture frames for displaying your drawings and paintings.

1

Cut a piece of cardboard the size you want your frame to be. Glue your picture to the middle of it.

The cardboard needs to be at least 5cm (2in) taller and wider than your picture.

2

Cut two strips of thick paper for the top and bottom of the frame. Make sure they overlap your picture a little. Don't glue the strips down yet.

3

For the sides of the frame, cut two more pieces of thick paper, which fit between the top and the bottom strips.

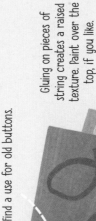

4

Next, decorate the strips. Here are lots of different suggestions for decorations...

You could draw or paint patterns...

...or stick on strips of fabric or patterned paper.

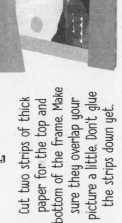

find a use for old buttons.

Gluing on pieces of string creates a raised texture. Paint over the top, if you like.

Cut squares from bright paper. Then, stick them on.

for a wood effect, paint the strip pale brown, then add wobbly lines in a darker brown.

Display your framed pictures...

MAKE A HANGER...

Cut a short piece of string. Then, use strong tape to stick it to the back of your frame.

The hanger hooks over a nail or pin, like this.

...OR MAKE A STAND

1 Cut a triangle from thin cardboard. Fold it in half lengthways.

The triangle should be a little shorter than your frame.

2 Cut off the bottom edges at a slight angle.

3 Then, glue one half to the back of the frame.

5

Wait until any paint or glue has dried, then glue the strips around the picture to finish the frame.

TWIG FRAMES

You could also decorate cardboard with twigs for a frame.

1 Collect any twigs you spot on the ground outdoors.

2 You could leave them different lengths or cut them into short strips.

3 Then, glue them onto the cardboard.

MAKE ART FROM DOTS

Did you know that you can paint pictures made up of lots of little dots? This technique is known as pointillism.

French artists Georges Seurat and Paul Signac invented this technique over 130 years ago. They thought they could make pictures more vivid with dots – rather than mixing colors as other artists did.

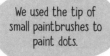

We used the tip of small paintbrushes to paint dots.

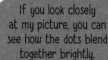

If you look closely at my picture, you can see how the dots blend together brightly.

Port of Saint-Tropez by Paul Signac, 1899

GET DOTTING!

Try out different combinations of dots, to see what they look like.

To paint your own dots...

...dip the tip of a paintbrush in some paint, then press it gently on the page, again and again.

Or use felt-tip pens or crayons to draw dots instead.

You could draw around a large coin to make circles to fill with dots.

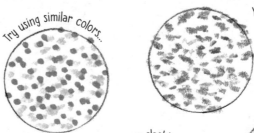

Try using similar colors...

You can use lots of colors together...

...and overlap dots too.

..or clashing colors..

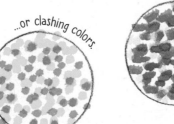

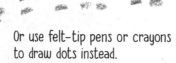

NOW MAKE A PICTURE

You could make a picture of a sailboat, inspired by Paul Signac's painting
on page 82. You'll need to make your picture in stages.

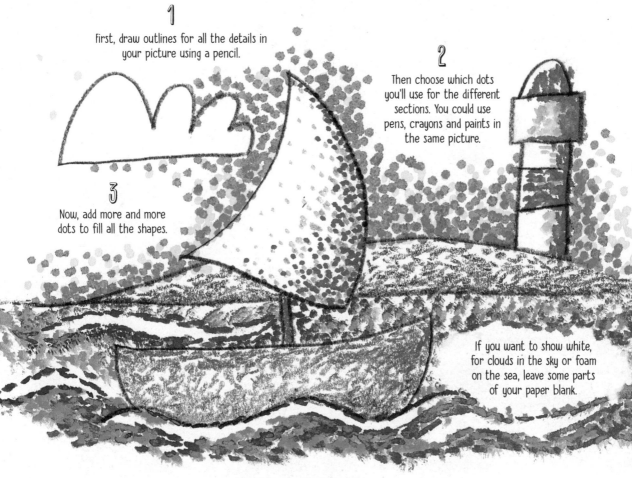

1

First, draw outlines for all the details in
your picture using a pencil.

2

Then choose which dots
you'll use for the different
sections. You could use
pens, crayons and paints in
the same picture.

3

Now, add more and more
dots to fill all the shapes.

If you want to show white,
for clouds in the sky or foam
on the sea, leave some parts
of your paper blank.

PIXEL PICTURES

Pictures on screens and digital photos are made up of dots too...

Lots of different colored
dots make up the color
of this gull's beak.

These dots are known as PIXELS.
They're very small, but you can
see them if you zoom in...

Pixels are actually
square shaped, so
they fit together
without any gaps.

TAKE RUBBINGS

If you find interesting textures on surfaces, you can make pictures with them by taking rubbings. You'll need crayons, chalks or pencils – and some paper.

How to rub

 1

Place a piece of paper over the surface. Tape it down with masking tape.

 2

Hold a crayon or piece of chalk on its side and rub it firmly over the paper...

...or hold a pencil at an angle and rub it from side to side.

Things to rub

You could look for several objects or surfaces to make rubbings like these...

Bubble wrap

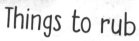
Bark

Bricks

Coins

floor or wall tiles

lace or textured fabric

Manhole covers

Scrunch then rub

You can also do a rubbing on a crumpled piece of paper to reveal a pattern of creases.

1 First, scrunch up the paper.

2 Unfold the paper to make it flat.

3 Rub a crayon on its side across the paper.

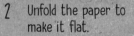

The creases will appear as white, spidery lines.

Now rub a chalk to make a "blueprint"...

In the late 19th and early 20th centuries, architects made copies of their designs using chemicals that reacted to light. This technique was known as blueprinting because the copied designs appeared as white lines on a blue background. Here's how to make your own pictures inspired by blueprints. You'll need some blue paper and a white chalk...

1 Find a picture of a building in an old magazine or newspaper and cut it out.

leave space around the building.

2 Then, rub white chalk all over the back of the picture you cut out.

3 Place the picture, chalk side down, on a piece of blue paper. Keep it in place with pieces of masking tape.

If you don't have any blue paper, you could use white paper instead. You'll need to use a blue, red, green or any other colored chalk in step 2.

4 Draw over the outline of the building and all the details you want to copy, pressing down heavily with a pencil.

Use a ruler to draw straight lines.

5 Remove the tape. Then, carefully lift the picture off the paper.

The parts of the building you've drawn over should appear as white lines.

85

DRAW IN PROPORTION

Drawings of people look more realistic if the different body parts are the right size in relation, or proportion, to each other. Here's a simple way to master the rules of proportion...

1

First, divide a piece of paper into eight rows by folding it in half, from top to bottom...

...once...

...twice...

...and three times.

Then, unfold it.

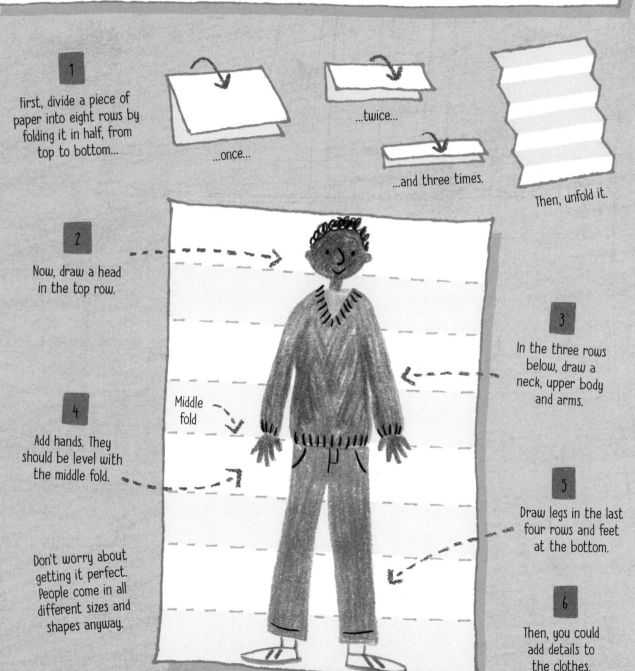

2

Now, draw a head in the top row.

3

In the three rows below, draw a neck, upper body and arms.

4

Add hands. They should be level with the middle fold.

Middle fold

Don't worry about getting it perfect. People come in all different sizes and shapes anyway.

5

Draw legs in the last four rows and feet at the bottom.

6

Then, you could add details to the clothes.

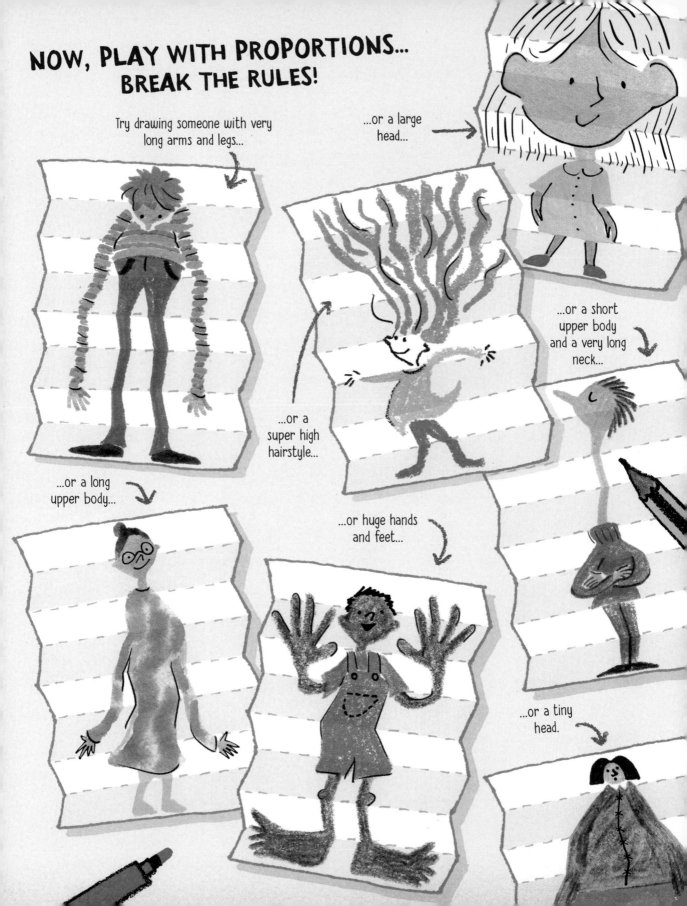

NOW, PLAY WITH PROPORTIONS...
BREAK THE RULES!

Try drawing someone with very long arms and legs...

...or a large head...

...or a short upper body and a very long neck...

...or a super high hairstyle...

...or a long upper body...

...or huge hands and feet...

...or a tiny head.

PRINT, PRINT AND PRINT AGAIN

There are all sorts of things you can use as stamps and blocks for printing pictures. Follow the same technique whatever you're using.

STAMPS, BLOCKS AND MORE

You can print with...

bottles and
bottle lids

shapes cut out
from cardboard

rubber bands,
around a small box

old sponges, cut into
shapes with scissors

bubble wrap

erasers

newspaper,
scrunched up
into balls

lettuce leaves

Cut out shapes
from bubble wrap
before you print
with them.

HOW TO PRINT

1
Put some liquid paint on an old kitchen towel.

2
Spread out the paint with a brush.

3
Press the block or stamp you're using into the paint gently...

4
...then press it onto some paper.

To make a print like this one, wrap lots of rubber bands around a box.

To make prints that fade, press down the block again without adding more paint...

...and again...

...and again.

88

The ridges on corrugated cardboard make textured prints. Cut out each shape you want to print first.

Use the base of a bottle, as well as its lid.

Try printing an ear shape with a stick of celery on its end.

Rotate the celery to print the other ear.

Print eyebrows with the end of an eraser.

Scrunch up paper to dab on freckles.

You could use the outer leaves of a lettuce or a cabbage to shape a hairstyle.

You could squash a cardboard tube, then use one of its ends to print an ear like this.

All the noses in these pictures are made from sponge prints.

89

PUT ON AN ART SHOW

When you've drawn and painted lots of pictures, you could stage a mini exhibition. Invite your friends and family to come and admire your works of art.

CHOOSING YOUR VENUE

You don't need lots of space. In fact, you can open a gallery almost anywhere.

You could prop up your pictures on shelves...

ART on the SHELF

Give your gallery a name and make a sign for it.

...or attach them to your bedroom door with masking tape.

THE OPEN DOOR GALLERY

Maybe you could use the inside of a cabinet door for your display?

Lucy's Art Box

PLANNING A SHOW

Art shows often have a theme that links together all the pictures on show.

Pick a theme, such as winter or food. Then make up a title inspired by it.

On a piece of paper, write a guide for visitors to read. Include a few sentences about the theme of your show and the works on display.

SNOW TIME

GOOD ENOUGH TO EAT

The artists involved in this exhibition painted the treats they love most to make a feast for your eyes...

You could ask your friends to make pictures, based on the theme you choose.

ALL ABOUT THE ART

Write exhibit labels for the pictures on display. For each work, include a title, the artist's name, and when it was made.

Quotations can help visitors feel as if they understand what the artist was thinking.

Pillow Fight
by Jamie Inglis, 2020

Jamie Inglis wants to be an artist when he grows up. With this picture he tried to capture the energy and fun of a pillow fight.

You could give information about the artist and what inspired them, too.

Penguin Parade
by Freddie Bolt, last week

Freddie Bolt said of this work, "Doesn't this picture make you wonder what the penguins are saying to each other?"

Turn to pages 80–81 for lots of ideas for how you can frame each picture to show it at its best.

Untitled
by Isabella Dennis, yesterday

Isabella Dennis argues that, "paintings don't have to show views or people to be interesting."

If you can't think of a title, just write "Untitled."

Daydreaming
by Sarah Spoon, March 2020

Sarah Spoon's paintings are inspired by the family cat, Tilly.

Write in the third person, as "she," "he," or "the artist," even if you're writing about yourself.

You could leave out a notebook for visitors to write their comments.

COMMENTS, PLEASE!

AND IF YOU'RE STILL BORED...

INVENT WEIRD TYPES OF WEATHER

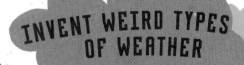

Doodle flowers falling from clouds...

...a "rainbow" made up of different shades of blue...

...or thunderbolt snakes.

MIX UP YOUR PAINTS

You could try painting a rose with a red stem and a green flower...

...or a fried egg with a white yolk...

...or a black cheetah with yellow spots.

MAKE A SELF-PORTRAIT

Dutch artist Rembrandt van Rijn made around 90 self-portraits. Take inspiration from him and try drawing yourself again and again. How different do you look each time?

You could use photographs to draw from – or look in a mirror.

DRAW ON A BALLOON

1 Pump up a balloon until it's only partly inflated.

Pinch the end between your fingers to stop any air from coming out.

2 Then, draw a picture on the balloon with a marker.

Rest the balloon on a table to keep it steady as you draw.

3 Next, let go of the balloon, so it deflates. Wait a few minutes for the ink to dry.

4 Now fill the balloon with air and tie a knot.

You could copy this owl!

Your picture will get wider and taller.

SEPARATE INKS

You may be surprised to learn that most colored inks are actually made up of lots of different colors. Try this experiment to find out about the inks in your felt-tip pens.

1 Fold a piece of paper towel in half.

2 Draw a row of short lines with different colored felt-tip pens near the bottom edge.

3 Dip the bottom of the paper in a little water for a few seconds, then leave it to dry. Watch what happens...

Plate

4 The inks dissolve on the wet paper and spread out. They separate into the different colors each ink contains.

TRY
MIXED-MEDIA ART

Page 73

Page 56

CARROT NOSE

Page 75

Some works of art are made using more than one type of material or method. This is known as mixed-media art.

Page 47

Choose several different drawing and painting techniques from this book. Then combine them together to make a hodgepodge picture.

DRAW OR PAINT YOUR DREAMS

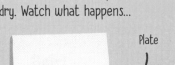

If you remember any of the things you dream about at night, you could make a picture of them the next day.

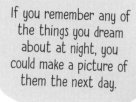

DRAW
UPSIDE DOWN

Turn your book upside down, then try to copy this cat. Copying pictures in this way makes you LOOK more closely and DRAW more accurately.

CHECK YOUR ANSWERS

34–35 TRAIN TO BE A RENAISSANCE ARTIST

COPYCAT

Apprentice C has copied the pose the best.

Bird is facing the wrong way.

left arm is too straight.

No mistakes here!

68–69 SOLVE PICTURE PUZZLES

NON-STOP DRAWING

There's more than one way to solve these picture puzzles. But you could draw each one following these steps...

1 First draw all the outer lines starting from here... ...then draw the lines inside.

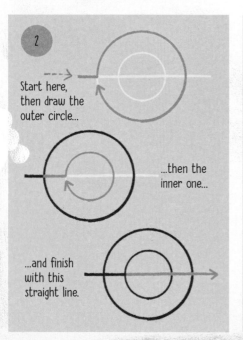

2 Start here, then draw the outer circle... ...then the inner one... ...and finish with this straight line.

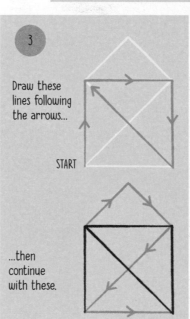

3 Draw these lines following the arrows... START ...then continue with these.

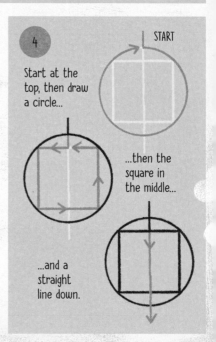

4 Start at the top, then draw a circle... START ...then the square in the middle... ...and a straight line down.

VISIT USBORNE QUICKLINKS

The internet is jam-packed with EVEN MORE drawing and painting ideas, but they're hidden among lots of boring stuff. For links to exciting and inspiring websites, go to Usborne Quicklinks at usborne.com/Quicklinks and type in the title of this book.

You'll find links to websites where you can...

Make paintbrushes from twigs

Explore an art gallery

Meet famous artists

And draw lots of faces

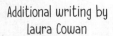

Please follow the internet safety guidelines at Usborne Quicklinks. Children should be supervised online.

Usborne Publishing is not responsible and does not accept liability for the availability or content of any website other than its own, or for any exposure to harmful, offensive or inaccurate material which may appear on the Web. Usborne Publishing will have no liability for any damage or loss caused by viruses that may be downloaded as a result of browsing the sites it recommends.

Additional illustrations by Colleen Larmour, Clover Robin and Robbie Cathro

Additional design by Claire Morgan, Laura Bridges and Josephine Thompson

Additional writing by Laura Cowan

Edited by Jane Chisholm

American edition edited by Carrie Armstrong

Photographs on cover, p46 and p47 © Vladamir Pogorelov/Dreamstime.com, © Denis Zhengal/Dreamstime.com; p1, pp46–47 and p81 © Chernetskya/Dreamstime.com; p5 and p47 © Bluwarrior/Dreamstime.com; p20 © MirasWonderland/Shutterstock, © Supoj Buranaprapapong/Dreamstime.com, © Elena Rostunova/Dreamstime.com, © Scaliger/Dreamstime.com; p42 © Toby Gibson/Dreamstime.com, © Jolanta Wojcicka/Dreamstime.com, © fiona Ayerst/Dreamstime.com; p46 © Wdnetagency/Dreamstime.com, © AtSkwongPhoto/Shutterstock; p47 © Luca Pape/Dreamstime.com; p82 © Granger Historical Picture Archive/Alamy Stock Photo; p83 © forGaby/Shutterstock

NON-STOP DRAWING (CONTINUED)

Follow the direction of the arrows as you draw the lines in each step.

START

ROOFTOPS

Group 2 matches view B.
Group 3 matches view A.

The missing view would look like this.

FROM TWO TO FOUR

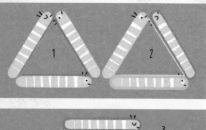

FAST FOX

The outlines show how the five triangles fit together.

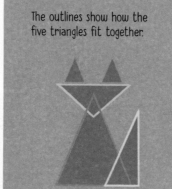

SHEEP PEN PUZZLE

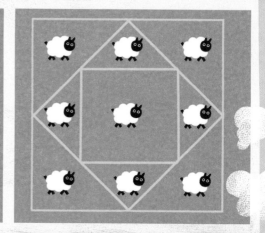

FAMOUS FLOORPLANS

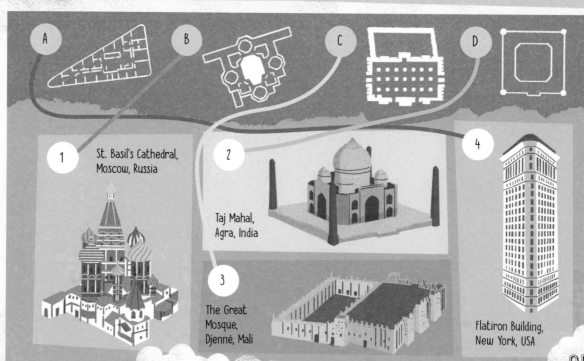

A   B   C   D

1 St. Basil's Cathedral, Moscow, Russia

2 Taj Mahal, Agra, India

3 The Great Mosque, Djenné, Mali

4 Flatiron Building, New York, USA